A SHORT HISTORY
OF PSYCHIATRY

PHILIPPE PINEL,
Né le 20 Avril 1745.

PINEL

A SHORT HISTORY OF PSYCHIATRY

by

ERWIN H. ACKERKNECHT

Professor of the History of Medicine
University of Zürich

Second, revised edition

Translated from the German by
S U L A   W O L F F

H A F N E R   P U B L I S H I N G   C O M P A N Y
NEW YORK AND LONDON
1968

Original edition 1959
Second, revised edition 1968

Printed and Published by
HAFNER PUBLISHING COMPANY, INC.
31 East 10th Street
New York, N.Y. 10003

Library of Congress Catalogue Card Number: 68-31630

Printed in U.S.A.

This book was set by Topel Typographic Corporation, New York,
and printed by Noble Offset Printers, Inc., New York, N.Y. 10003.

To the memory of Ruth Benedict

CONTENTS

LIST OF PLATES

PREFACE TO THE SECOND EDITION

THE nine years that have passed since the first appearance of this book have seen its translation into English, Spanish and Japanese. Much detailed work has been done in the field, to which my pupils and I have contributed. I have attempted to incorporate this new knowledge into my book without disturbing its overall structure and I have also tried as far as this was possible to take note of the suggestions of my critics who were on the whole friendly. One negative comment, however, which was often made surprised me: that the history of psychiatry can be written only by psychiatrists. So far the efforts of psychiatrists turned historians have not been altogether successful, and since when must one be a politician or a soldier to write political or military history, a creative artist to write the history of art or literature?

I was glad that despite some reservations, my small book has been found useful by many psychiatrists and I hope this will continue. I would like here to thank my wife, Edit, for her many stimulating suggestions.

ERWIN H. ACKERKNECHT

Zürich
Spring, 1967

PREFACE TO THE FIRST EDITION

PSYCHIATRY is more than a medical speciality. 150 years ago it was described by Reil as one of the three basic disciplines of medicine, together with internal medicine and surgery. One might even go further and say that there is no case of illness in which the psychiatrist has not some contribution to make. The social significance of psychiatry, too, can hardly be exaggerated. In the United States, for example, 50% to 70% of available hospital beds are required for mentally ill patients.

Nevertheless, to write the history of psychiatry is an unrewarding task. The psychiatric historian cannot as yet indulge in the paeans of progress and achievement which nowadays usually make the work of his colleague in general medicine so much easier. As Griesinger said a hundred years ago, and his gloomy statement is still unfortunately often true today, we know as little about mental disorders as men knew about diseases of the chest in the days before Laennec. One is indeed frequently tempted to wonder whether the well-known "historical spiral" is in this case just a simple circular movement. This is, of course, the fault neither of the historians nor of psychiatrists. Psychiatry is the youngest branch of medicine. For historical reasons, which will be more closely examined below, its renaissance occurred two hundred years later than that of the other medical disciplines. In addition, psychiatry still suffers from the hostility which has always been directed against the mentally ill and against their physicians. Above all, psychiatry is concerned with the most difficult medico-physiological problem: that of the body-mind relationship which has remained unsolved to the present day. Anatomy, physiology, morbid anatomy and chemistry, which have contributed so much to other disciplines during the last hundred years, have been far less helpful in the elucidation of mental illnesses. For this reason large numbers of different and often dogmatic schools continue to exist in psychiatry today, as they existed in internal medicine in earlier times. This increases the difficulties of surveying and of understanding the subject but is, of course, no reason for abandoning the study of psychiatry or of its history; on the contrary, it makes it perhaps all the more necessary. But it seemed best to point out these difficulties frankly in the hope that the reader will thereby be better able to understand both the short-comings of this book and its subject matter. Indeed, just because progress in psychiatry has been so very slow, study of the past may have more to offer to the psychiatrist of today than to his medical and surgical colleagues.

A further obstacle in the way of writing a short history of psychiatry is the fact that very few basic studies, and even fewer good ones, have been carried out in this field, particularly in recent times. I have, therefore, had to depend primarily upon my own studies of original sources and to present many summaries of texts of the older writers. At the same time, for reasons of space I have had to limit myself in this to the writings of a few men of particular importance. This does not mean that I support the "great man" theory of history. Great men are made possible only by the work of their contemporaries and of their predecessors. If Pinel or Kraepelin or Freud had never lived others would have carried out their work with greater or lesser distinction. This is not to deny that these great men were the most able representatives of the psychiatry of their day and that they merit the closest study in a short historical review. In reporting the older texts, I have attempted to reproduce the sum total of the opinions expressed in them and have not, as is unfortunately the current trend, merely selected what appears to be modern in them.

I have tried to be as brief as possible and am, therefore, liable to be reproached for various omissions. I am however encouraged to hope that because my book is short, it will be read; and this seems to me to be a reasonable aim. Because I wished and needed to be concise, I have had to limit myself to the presentation of only a small selection of the many great names and of the abundant literature of the nineteenth century. In dealing with the twentieth century however I have restricted myself still further and have not ventured to do more than touch on its basic trends. This is not only for reasons of space: I am convinced that it is almost impossible for an historian to produce anything of value if he is too close to the period he is studying. As a medical historian I have here concerned myself only with medical psychiatry, although a philosophical psychiatry has been known to exist since the time of the Greeks. The decision to limit myself in this way was relatively easy to make, since it seems to me that philosophical psychiatry has never been of much help in practice. I have perhaps not always shown the proper respect for attempts, so common in the history of psychiatry, to conceal ignorance behind new words and a spurious profundity. It is high time, however, that someone revealed what stuff the emperor's new clothes are made of.

Although, even in the twentieth century, psychiatric achievements have lagged behind those of internal medicine and surgery, the last fifty years have seen the emergence of much that is promising. Psychiatry has always been in many ways the most human and most interesting of the medical sciences. I venture to hope that the reader will find at least a reflection of this in my small book.

I am very grateful to Dr. Joachim Bodamer of Winnental and to Professor Victor Gourevitch of Chicago, for sparing the time to read and criticise my manuscript, despite our basic differences in outlook.

ERWIN H. ACKERKNECHT

Zürich
May, 1957

BIBLIOGRAPHICAL COMMENTS

WE would like to draw the reader's attention to the following more recent general accounts of the history of psychiatry:

In German

BIRNBAUM, K., *Geschichte der Psychiatrischen Wissenschaft,* in BUMKE, O., *Handbuch der Geisteskrankheiten,* Vol. I, pp. 11-49, Berlin, 1928. DE BOOR, W., *Psychiatrische Systematik seit Kahlbaum,* Berlin, 1954. KIRCHHOFF, TH., *Grundriss einer Geschichte der deutschen Irrenpflege,* Berlin, 1890. Idem., *Geschichte der Psychiatrie,* in ASCHAFFENBURG, G., *Handbuch der Psychiatrie,* Vol. I, pp. 1-48, Vienna, 1912. Idem., *Deutsche Irrenaerzte,* 2 vols., Berlin, 1921 and 1924. KOLLE, K., *Grosse Nervenaerzte,* 3 vols., Stuttgart, 1956, 1959, 1963. KORNFELD, S., *Geschichte der Psychiatrie,* in Puschmann's *Handbuch der Geschichte der Medizin,* ed. M. Neuburger and J. Pagel, Vol. III, pp. 600-728, Jena, 1905. KRAEPELIN, E., *Hundert Jahre der Psychiatrie.* Zscht. ges. Neur. 38, pp. 161-275, 1918. LAEHR, H., *Gedenktage der Psychiatrie,* Berlin, 1899. Idem., *Die Literatur der Psychiatrie, Neurologie und Psychologie von 1459-1799,* 2 vols., Berlin, 1900. LEIBBRAND, W., and WETTLEY, A., *Der Wahnsinn,* Freiburg, Munich, 1961. LESKY, E., *Die Wiener Medizinische Schule im 19. Jahrhundert* (Chapter on Psychiatry), Graz, Cologne, 1965. SCHULTZ, J. H., *Psychotherapie, Leben und Werk grosser Aerzte,* Stuttgart, 1952. WYSS, D., *Die tiefenpsychologischen Schulen,* Goettingen, 1961.

In English

ALEXANDER, F. G., and SELESNICK, T. S., *The History of Psychiatry,* New York, 1966. BROMBERG, W., *Man above Humanity: a History of Psychotherapy,* Philadelphia, 1954. DEUTSCH, A., *The Mentally Ill in America,* New York, 1937. HALL, J. K., etc., Editors, *One Hundred Years of American Psychiatry,* New York, 1944. HUNTER, R., and MACALPINE, I., *Three Hundred Years of Psychiatry 1535-1860,*

xi

London, 1963. JONES, K., *Lunacy, Law and Conscience 1744-1845*, London, 1955. Idem., *Mental Health and Social Policy 1845-1959*, London, 1960. LEIGH, D., *The Historical Development of British Psychiatry*, Vol. I, Oxford, 1961. LEWIS, N., *A Short History of Psychiatry*, New York, 1944. MORA, G., *The History of Psychiatry: a cultural and bibliographic survey*, in *Psychoanalytic Review*, 52, 1965, pp. 299-328. SCHNECK, J., *A History of Psychiatry*, Springfield, 1960. TUKE, D. H., *Chapters on the History of the Insane in the British Isles*, London, 1882. WHITWELL, J. R., *Historical Notes on Psychiatry*, London, 1936. ZILBOORG, G., *History of Medical Psychology*, New York, 1941.

In French

BARUK, H., *La Psychiatrie Française de Pinel à Nosjours*, Paris, 1967. FOUCAULT, M., *Historie de la Folie à l'âge Classique*, Paris, 1961. LAIGNEL-LAVASTINE, M. et VINCHON, J., *Les Malades de L'Esprit et leurs Médecins, du XVIe à XIXe siècle*, Paris, 1930. SEMELAIGNE, R., *Les Grands Aliénistes Français*, Paris, 1891. Idem., *Aliénistes et Philanthropes*, Paris, 1912. Idem., *Les Pionniers de la Psychiatrie Française avant et après Pinel*, 2 vols., Paris, 1930-1932. RITTI, A., *Histoire des Travaux de la Société Médico-psychologique et Eloges de ses Membres*, 2 vols., Paris, 1913, 1914. VIÉ, J., *Histoire Generale de la Médecine*, Paris, 1949, Vol. III, pp. 278-322.

The excellent recent articles by H. Ellenberger and George Rosen on the history of psychiatry will I hope be available soon, as abstracts or as collected papers in book form.

Chapter 1

ETHNOLOGICAL COMMENTS

In this book we shall be concerned with the history of psychiatry, that is with the science of mental diseases. We can therefore be brief in our discussion of primitive ideas which have no claim to be scientific. The concept of disease held by primitive peoples is totally different from ours. They do not, with a few exceptions,[1] have mental illnesses in our sense. Disease is to them a monistic concept; there is no division between diseases of the body and the mind, but the nature of disease is the same, whatever the symptoms. Almost all illnesses are attributed to the intervention of supernatural forces such as evil spirits, gods, witches or magicians. Illnesses of all kinds are frequently explained on the basis of possession by evil spirits, and this is particularly so in the case of mental illnesses. So long as one can believe in spirits this explanation carries conviction. It can help one to understand fairly easily how quantities of strange, obscene and nonsensical material can spring from what until then had been a familiar and reasonable human being. One might even ask oneself whether this explanation which is used by many primitives for all diseases, did not originate from empirical observations made on cases of mental illness.

The methods of treatment used are of the greatest interest to the modern observer. Primitive societies are familiar with several effective drugs and several effective physical methods of treatment, such as massage and some surgical procedures. These are however used only within the framework of magico-religious treatments which consist of conjuring, magical charms, invocations, songs and dances. This follows naturally from the basic concept of the primitives that all illnesses are of supernatural origin. We can explain the efficacy

---

[1] Wieschhoff, H. A., *Concepts of Abnormality among the Ibo of Nigeria*, J. *Am. Orient. Soc.* 63: 262, 1943.

of these measures (and they are often quite successful) only on the basis of their psychotherapeutic elements. A closer study of these treatment rituals reveals that they involve a great deal of confession and suggestion, and are often not very different even in form from our methods of treatment.

The personality of the therapist for the mentally ill is determined by the concepts of illness existing within each society. His roles change in different communities from those of the magician or medicine man, to the later roles of priest, general practitioner, lay healer or medical specialist. How primitive tribes contained their chronically aggressive patients is unknown. No doubt at times they were put to death, but the regular killing of such patients was as rare as it was to kill the aged or those with incurable diseases.

If we dwell a little longer on ethnographic material, we are only following an old psychiatric tradition. From Benjamin Rush and J. C. Prichard to Kraepelin and A. Marie, psychiatrists have been attracted to comparative psychiatry. In recent times too several ethnologists, particularly in North America (where they call themselves cultural anthropologists) have I think contributed greatly to our understanding of the nature of mental illness, its social origins, and in particular the relativity of its symptoms. Most noteworthy are the works of Ruth Benedict, E. Sapir, I. A. Hallowell and their successors.[2] Their argument briefly is as follows: we look upon certain behavioral phenomena, such as ideas of persecution, grandiose ideas, states of ecstasy, hallucinations, compulsive ideas and marked changes of facial expression and of gesture, as symptoms of mental illness. But the study of foreign cultures has shown that all these so-called symptoms can, under different circumstances, be regarded different place and at a different time. For instance, ideas of perse-as normal, just as so-called "pathological tissues" can be normal in a cution are normal among the Dobuans, grandiose ideas among the Kwakiutl, and hallucinations among the Siberians and the Zulus. Homosexuality is regarded as normal by many tribes who even give their transvestites a legal status, known as Berdache. The belief in taboo often leads to behavior which we would consider to be com-

---

[2] Those interested in a detailed exposition of this material, and a comprehensive bibliography, are referred to my article, *"Psychopathology, Primitive Medicine and Primitive Culture,"* reprinted by Bobbs Merril, 1962, *Bull. Hist. Med.* 14: 30-67, 1943; and to Ruth Benedict's most important and easily accessible work: "Patterns of Culture."

pulsive. Conversely people commonly considered to be abnormal by these societies, such as kind and generous individuals in Dobu, would be regarded by us as normal. We have therefore thought it useful to introduce into comparative psychopathology the terms autonormal and autopathological on the one hand, and heteronormal and heteropathological on the other. Autonormal and autopathological would apply to individuals regarded as normal or pathological, respectively, by their own society; heteronormal and heteropathological to those regarded as normal or pathological, respectively, by members of another society observing them.

It follows that what is psychologically normal depends to a high degree on the attitudes of different societies. The same is true incidentally of crime. The criterion by which a person in any society is judged to be mentally ill is not primarily the presence of certain unvarying and universally occurring symptoms. It depends rather on whether the affected individual is capable of some minimum of adaptation and social functioning within his society, or whether the psychological change has progressed to such an extent that he has become an outcast in his society.

The relativity of symptoms can be observed in historical as well as in ethnological material. Henry E. Sigerist[3] pointed out many years ago that the troubadour who appeared quite normal to his contemporaries would by us be regarded as insane. The same is true for many other characters of the Middle Ages and of the early Renaissance, e.g. the ecstatic religionists, the witch hunters and the ascetic puritans. There is little doubt that the normal man of today would have seemed abnormal in many earlier centuries. This may be related to the fact that the nature of mental diseases is apparently changing with the course of time. Thus Jaspers, for instance, sees schizophrenia as the predominant mental illness of the present day, whereas hysteria occurred more frequently in the nineteenth and earlier centuries.

This relativity of symptoms is seen in our own society in relation to differences of social class and status. If a poor peasant believes in the evil eye, one can by no means assume that he is mentally ill. If the same belief is held by a university professor, this assumption becomes inevitable. Modes of behavior regarded as normal in artists

---

[3] *"Psychopathologie und Kulturwissenschaft" Abh. aus der Neurol. Psychiatrie, Psychol. u. ihren Grenzgeb.* Vol. 61, p. 140-146, 1930.

or adolescents would be regarded as abnormal in average adults. In this connection it is interesting to note that Kinsey found clear differences in sexual behavior and in concepts of normality in this field among the different classes in the United States of America, despite the fact that there are fewer psychological class differences in the United States than in any other modern society. A. B. Hollingshead and F. C. Redlich (*Social Class and Mental Illness*, New York, 1958) found significant differences in the incidence of neuroses in upper and lower class patients. Fifty per cent of the former patients were neurotic, compared with ten per cent of the latter.

It must be pointed out here that in spite of apparent similarities in outward guise and in content, there is a fundamental difference between the patterns of behavior seen in primitives and those observed in the insane. The ideas of persecution of the average Dobuan and the ideas of grandeur of a Kwakiutl are not held by them as individuals, but because each one thinks within the conceptual framework of his culture, and because such ideas are held by the majority of their tribes. The exceptional individual, who in our culture is the victim of ideas of grandeur or of persecution, does not share the concepts of his culture. On the contrary he is unable to make these concepts his own. This point should also be remembered when comparing the often apparently very similar artistic productions of the insane and of children on the one hand, with those of primitives on the other.

This is not of course to deny the possibility that behind this multiplicity of symptoms there may lie in all societies the same biological disposition to disease—an absolute abnormality per se. The difficulty is that we have no absolute biological criteria for diagnosing or classifying even the most widespread psychoses and neuroses and are therefore forced to rely largely on their symptomatology and on their effect on the patient's capacity to conform to the society in which he lives. This difficulty is not lessened, as far as comparative pathology is concerned, by the fact that psychoses known to have an organic basis, such as general paresis, alcoholism, and senile dementia, do not exist among savages.

The relativity of symptoms is by no means limited to the field of mental diseases. In somatic medicine also it is often not the absolute state of affairs but society's evaluation of it which decides whether a biological variation is to be regarded as a disease or not. It did not occur to the Chinese of classical times to look upon the crippled feet of their women as signs of illness. Many African tribes do not regard infestation with intestinal worms or yaws as illnesses, probably because they are so common. It is reported, somewhat grotesquely, that among some South American Indians a very disfiguring spirochaetal infection of the skin, known as pinto, is so widespread that almost all men suffer from it. The few who escape infection are regarded as ill and are precluded from marriage. It has been shown historically that malaria was so prevalent in many parts of the world in the nineteenth century (e.g. in the Mississippi Valley), that it was no longer regarded as a disease. The same was true for eczema among children in the eighteenth century.

We must assume therefore that the prevalence and definition of mental disease depend upon social circumstances. It follows that mental illnesses must vary in form and importance in different tribes, cultures and civilizations. This is indeed the case. There are however no tribes in which all members are insane, nor are there tribes in which mental illness or suicide are unknown. The latter assumption, once widespread, is merely a vestige of Rousseau's illusion of the "noble savage." Hallowell on the contrary has rightly pointed out that ideas about supernatural forces can at times have beneficial and healing effects on mental illnesses, but can also result in pathogenic fears and conflicts. In addition it must not be forgotten that most of the so-called savages are, or were, observed not in their "natural state" but in a state of "acculturation," as it is called in North America, that is at a moment in their history in which their own culture was threatened both physically and psychologically by a foreign culture. This state appears to encourage the development of individual and of collective psychoses.

Although therefore mental illness appears to exist everywhere, many serious observers have pointed out that some forms of mental illness common in our culture, for example schizophrenia, are not found in such diverse parts of the world as Melanesia, Brazil, Central Africa or among the North American Indians. The attempt, which has recently once again become fashionable, to force a variety of different mental illnesses into the category of schizophrenia is essentially artificial. We have already mentioned that certain organic psychoses are not found among primitives, partly because of their short life span. On the other hand serious observers have pointed out the prevalence of mental illnesses among some primitives, e.g. among the Siberian tribes. On the whole however our material is too meagre, both in quantity and in quality, to enable us to go beyond such generalizations. In some tribes it may well be possible that mental illnesses are rare because of favorable conditions. In others it may be that psychotherapy is effective, or that the sick are killed outright.[4] In the absence of a local distinction between mental and physical diseases it is also possible that psychiatrically untrained visitors may often have overlooked endemic forms of mental illnesses and may have described some as physical illnesses. We possess only a single statistical example in this whole field, and even this is of doubtful value in several respects. N. Skliar and K. Starikova (*Zur vergleichenden Psychiatrie: Arch. f. Psychiatrie und Nervenkrankheiten*, 88: 554-85, 1929) compared the incidence of mental illnesses among seven national groups in the province of Astrakhan. Two of the groups, the Kalmucks and the Kirghiz, remained quite primitive for a considerable period of time. The results were as follows:

(1) The incidence of mental illness was very low amongst these tribes at the beginning of the period reported on: in fact it was almost non-existent. Kalmucks 1850: 0.01%. Kirghiz hospital admission rate 1890: 0.4 per 100,000.

(2) Contact with civilization, such as occurred after 1850, was accompanied by a steady rise in the figures (Kalmucks 1898: 0.07%. Kirghiz hospital admission rates 1927: 3.0 per 100,-000). The greater the distance between a Kalmuck tribe and the civilized areas, the lower were the figures. The incidence of mental diseases in both tribes was far lower than that of the neighboring, civilized communities (Kalmucks 2-14 per 100,000; Tartars 3-60; Armenians 90; Jews 50; Russians and Persians 100 per 100,000). The influence of civilization was not attributable to alcohol or syphilis. In both tribes syphilis was endemic but general paresis did not occur. The Kalmuck tribe had always been alcoholic; the moslem Kirghiz continued to be abstinent.

(3) Dementia praecox continued to be rare among the primitives (Kalmucks 2.6% of all mental illnesses; Kirghiz 1.9%, compared with 6.4% among the Russians and 20% among the

[4] Koty, J., *Die Behandlung der Alten und Kranken bei den Naturvölkern*, Stuttgart, 1934.

Armenians). Neither hysteria nor general paresis was observed among these tribes.

(4) Whilst these tendencies were found in both tribes, they differed considerably with respect to their prevalence among men and women. Among the Kalmucks there were twice as many women mentally ill as men; among the Kirghiz suffering from mental illness the sex ratio reached the unusually high figure of eight men to one woman. Between 1890 and 1902, five to thirty times as many Kalmucks were admitted to hospital as were Kirghiz. In 1925 to 1927 these figures were three to ten.

It is worth noting that some forms of mental illness which occur in primitive peoples are difficult or impossible to fit into our own categories of disease. There is first of all Amok, the familiar murderous psychosis first observed among the Malay but later also among South American Indians, Melanesians, Siberians, Indians and also the Masai. A neurosis characterized above all by echolalia and echopraxia was first observed in Siberia and was described in climatic terms as Arctic hysteria, until it was found to occur frequently in East India, in the Philippines and in Madagascar. It is now generally referred to by the Malay name of "Latah." Imu, a disease of the Ainu, is a strange combination of Latah and Amok. A cannibalistic psychosis of North American Indians, in some ways reminiscent of the "Vaudoisie" of the fifteenth century,[5] has become known as "Windigo." Certain intoxicants, such as Indian hemp also of course evoke special psychoses. It is noteworthy that alcoholism can have different manifestations in different tribes. Perhaps the most remarkable of the psychoses observed among primitive people is that known as Thanatomania, or death by autosuggestion, in which the patient believes he has been bewitched and dies without visible organic changes. This has been described and studied under the name "Vodoo death" by the famous physiologist, W. B. Cannon.[6] In all these cases it is obvious that the nature of the illness is determined not by climate nor by racial factors but by the culture, that is, by the sum total of social relationships. Much has been written about mass psychoses among primitive people. But, as Griesinger has already pointed out, one must be careful to avoid

[5] Cesbron, H., *Histoire Critique de l'Hystérie*, Paris, 1909, p. 134.

[6] Cannon, W. B., *Vodoo Death.*, *Am. Anthropologist*, 44: 169, 1942.

misinterpreting purely religious movements as mass psychoses.

These ethnological considerations would be incomplete without some mention of the medicine man, the physician of the primitives, who is in many books still referred to as an epileptic, an hysteric, a neurotic, and even as an idiot. Such descriptions appear to be completely false and to be due to ignorance or misunderstanding. They are refuted by all present-day ethnologists who have had personal experience among savages. It is true that in a few parts of the world (particularly in Siberia and South-east Africa) individuals who are known to have experienced a psychosis later turn to the art of healing. But at the time of practising their profession, and perhaps because of their choice of profession, they are healthy, in the sense of being fully able to perform their social functions. Individuals who are suffering from a real mental disease are rejected as physicians by the natives themselves. The Siberian name of "Shaman" should be reserved for these individuals and not used indiscriminately for all medicine men. A further group of native practitioners appeared to previous untrained European observers to be pathological since they developed trance states and were possessed by helpful spirits. Such states, however, are autonormal in these tribes; are distinguished by the natives themselves from possession by evil spirits, that is, from hysterical or epileptic attacks; are regarded as desirable and are therefore in some measure encouraged. The great majority of medicine men seem to be normal even by our criteria. Indeed many trained ethnologists such as Elkin, Hallowell, Olbrecht, Warner, Seligman, Stoll and Shirokogoroff, have stressed their superior intelligence and complete normality, despite their ideas which we find so strange.

The assumption that medicine men or savages who believe in magic are mentally ill is only a special instance of the bad habit, so widespread in our society, of dismissing as psychopathological everything that is different and not at once open to our understanding. "The undefinable is regarded as psychopathic."

It seemed for a time as if psychiatry and ethnology[7] would con-

---

[7] The reader is referred to the following comprehensive expositions of the more recent relationships between ethnology and psychiatry: Kluckhohn, C. *The Influence of Psychiatry on Anthropology in America*, in "Hundred Years of American Psychiatry," New York, 1944, p. 589; Caudill, W., *Applied Anthropology in Medicine*, in "Anthropology Today," A. L. Kroeber ed. Chicago, 1953; Opler, M. R., *Culture, Psychiatry and Human Values*, Springfield, 1956.

tinue to benefit from each other, for example, when Malinowski showed that among the Trobrianders the so-called "Oedipus complex" was not directed against the father but against the authority figure of the mother's brother. But unfortunately most of the ethnologists who are interested in psychiatry have accepted with naive gullibility the tenets of psychoanalysis or one of its derivative schools, so that their later works are full of fantasy rather than fact.

Psychiatry itself has for some time recognized that psychological illnesses are socially determined, and the move away from an absolutism of symptoms began some hundred years ago. It cannot be denied, however, that in both directions the study of ethnographic material has been, and will continue to be, of great value.

CHAPTER II

GRECO-ROMAN PSYCHIATRY

THE history of psychiatry, like that of scientific medicine in general, really begins with the Greeks. The Greco-Roman outlook survived unchanged until the eighteenth century, and even today we still use a large part of the Greek nomenclature. While the great cultures of old, such as those of Egypt and Mesopotamia, vacillated between naturalistic and supernatural explanations of diseases, the Greeks declared themselves outspokenly in favor of naturalistic explanations and thus became the founders of scientific medicine and of psychiatry. This applies, of course, only to the Greek medical profession. In other spheres religious concepts continued to survive, and religious explanations of disease and methods of treatment were at least as common outside official medical practice in the Greek culture as in our own.

The introductory remarks to the Hippocratic book on epilepsy, the "sacred disease," are typical of the new outlook: "The position regarding the so-called sacred disease is as follows: It seems to me to be no more divine and no more sacred than other diseases, but, like other affections, it springs from natural causes . . . Those who first connected this illness with demons and described it as sacred seem to me no different from the conjurors, purificators, mountebanks and charlatans of our day, who pretend to great piety and superior knowledge. But such persons are merely concealing, under the cloak of godliness, their perplexity and their inability to afford any assistance." (Grimm, J. F. C., *The Works of Hippocrates,* Glogau, 1838, Vol. 2, p. 211.) In this way those formerly regarded as being possessed were now thought to be ill, and, according to the Greek ideas about illness, to be physically ill. Greek medicine, like primitive medicine, is monistic, only on a new and completely different basis.

Unfortunately for us there is a great poverty of Greco-Roman documents relating to mental illnesses. It is hard to say whether this is attributable to the loss of manuscripts or to a lack of interest in these diseases. Such material as does exist comes from the later period of antiquity; but it can no longer be assumed, as was done in the past, that this necessarily reflects an increase during that later period in the incidence of mental disorder. The two giants of Greek medicine, Hippocrates (460-377 B.C.) and Galen (130-201 A.D.), have left behind only occasional accounts relating to mental illnesses. Pinel blamed Galen for his lack of interest in psychiatry, which he said was the reason for the lack of progress in this field until the eighteenth century. What little Galen wrote about melancholia, for example, the three different localizations of the illness: in the brain, blood, or gastrointestinal tract ("vapors"), played an enormous role in medical tradition up to the eighteenth century. Our main sources are: Celsus (circa 30 A.D.), the Roman encyclopaedist, who in his book, *"De re medica,"* presents us with a chapter on the treatment of melancholia and of mania; and Aretaeus of Cappadocia (circa 150 A.D.) in whose book, *"Acute and Chronic Diseases,"* we find short chapters on the nature of melancholia and mania and on the treatment of phrenitis and melancholia. Our best source is the methodist, Soranus of Ephesus (circa 100 A.D.), whose two major works on acute and on chronic diseases have survived in a Latin translation by Caelius Aurelianus (circa 500 A.D.), of which there is an excellent English translation and edition by I. E. Drabkin (Chicago, 1950). The work on acute diseases contains several chapters on phrenitis and its treatment. That on chronic diseases contains chapters on mania and melancholia and their treatment. It is characteristic of the period that none of these authors wrote separate books on mental diseases, but incorporated their discussions of them in general medical works.

Greek medicine experienced many changes in the thousand years of its independent existence and produced many different points of view. Soranus himself was the adherent of only one of these: Methodism. His concepts, however, of the basic patterns of mental diseases are so similar to those of the other writers of the time that the best and easiest way of gaining some knowledge of Greek psychiatry is to begin with a summary of his ideas:[1]

[1] The "classical" theory of disease, as is well known (that of Hippocrates and Galen), is the theory of the four humors. The body consists of four different

According to Soranus, phrenitis is so called because the mind (*phren,* originally the diaphragm), that is, thinking is affected. Soranus begins with a critical review of the definitions of phrenitis given by Herophilus and by Asclepiades and then presents his own definition: an acute disease of the mind accompanied by acute fever, foolish gesticulations an a small, full pulse. We are thus obviously dealing with febrile delirium. Soranus then discusses in a typically Greek manner and with much clinical detail the arguments for and against the existence of prodromal signs of phrenitis such as insomnia, polyuria, headache, injected eyes, etc. He believes that there is no single specific sign but that one can predict the onset of this illness, which he regards as a very serious one, from a combination of such symptoms. He then turns to consider the differential diagnosis of phrenitis, mania, melancholia, pleurisy, pneumonia and mandrake and henbane poisoning. He asks how one can differentiate mania accompanied by fever from phrenitis, and how one can distinguish healthy sleep occurring during the course of phrenitis from the development of lethargy (coma) in this condition. Among other signs, the color and expression of the face, respiration, pulse, stance and body temperature should be taken into account.

He then turns to more theoretical considerations. As a methodist, he rejects as merely symptomatic the subdivision of phrenitis into gay and sad forms. He suggests instead a subdivision into phrenitis on the basis of status strictus (tension) and phrenitis occurring on the basis of status laxus (relaxation). Some writers he says, look for the seat of phrenitis in the brain, others in the head or in the aorta. Each in fact looks for it in the place which he believes to be the seat of the soul. Soranus himself regards phrenitis as a general disease.but admits that, on the basis of the symptoms, the head seems

---

juices: blood, yellow bile, black bile, and phlegm, which correspond to the four elements: air, fire, earth and water. To each humor belong two of the four qualities: hot, moist, dry and cold. One humor predominates in each of the four temperaments: the sanguine, choleric, melancholic and phlegmatic. All diseases are caused by a disturbance of equilibrium of the humors, by the predominance or failure of one of them. Melancholia, for example, is a disease caused by the hypothetical black bile. After 300 B.C., however, other schools and factions came into being in Greek medicine, and these developed a solidist pathology and attributed diseases to changes in the solid components of the body. The best known of these schools was Methodism, which regarded all illnesses as being caused by an abnormal constriction or relaxation of the body tissues (*status strictus and status laxus*).

to be the part most seriously affected and should therefore be the focus of attention.

In the treatment of phrenitis Soranus recommends isolation in a moderately light, warm and airy room, with high windows so that the patient cannot jump out. The following is characteristic of his undogmatic attitude: according to theory, phrenitis due to tension should be nursed in a well-lit room, whilst phrenitis due to exhaustion should be nursed in a dark room. But Soranus declares that if a patient reacts differently, then one should treat him in the manner which best suits his inclinations. In status strictus he must be kept awake. The attendants should enter into a few of his delusions, but should reject others. If insufficient attendants are available, the patient should be carefully fettered in order to keep him quiet. Soranus recommends warm poultices of oil, to be applied particularly to the head, and also careful blood-letting. On the third or fourth day the head should be shaved and treated with cupping, leeches and scarification. Passive exercises such as rocking and a careful diet are indicated. Wine should not be allowed.

One should maintain a serious attitude towards abnormally cheerful patients and a friendly one towards those who are downcast. Excitement which can evoke physical illness even in healthy people is to be avoided since there is very great danger that it might precipitate a relapse.

Soranus then deals in a polemic manner with the treatment methods advocated by other writers such as Diocles, Erasistratus, Heraclides, and especially Asclepiades, which differ from his own in certain details. When a state of stupor follows on phrenitis, he calls it lethargy. He uses the term catalepsy to denote stupor accompanied by fever. His description of catalepsy could fit that of meningitis. He then goes on to describe other acute illnesses such as pleurisy, pneumonia, apoplexy, ileus, tetanus, etc.

In his chapter on mania or insanity or raving madness, he reports that Plato recognized two forms of mania: one of divine origin and one due to physical exertion. He concerns himself only with the latter. His definition is: a disturbance of reason without fever. Mania is found most commonly in young men and least often in women and children. Some of the causes are latent. The demonstrable causes are over-exertion, licentiousness, alcoholism and absence of the relief afforded by bleeding from haemorrhoids or by menstruation.

This theory was maintained in all seriousness until the nineteenth century. Mania according to Soranus had the same prodromata as had epilepsy and apoplexy. It could occur continuously or in intermittent attacks. Its manifestations were fury, gaiety, sadness, silliness or anxiety, such as for example a persistent fear of falling into ditches. Some patients were unable to visit underground chambers on account of this fear. Patients in these deluded states may see themselves as sparrows, cockerels, earthenware vessels, gods, orators, actors, grains of corn, the centre of the universe, or as infants. The eyes are injected, the body is firm and abnormally strong. The symptoms suggest that mania is a physical disease affecting in particular the head, and is due to status strictus. Soranus rejects the view of the philosophers that mania is a disease of the soul (diaphysis) and attributes their therapeutic failures to their misconceptions. It will be remembered that Plato, in his *Charmides,* had paid a similar compliment to the physicians of his day when he accused them of inability either to understand or to cure mental diseases.

The description of the treatment of mania is basically similar to that of phrenitis and therefore need not be repeated. Soranus makes a few minor additions such as listening to dripping water in cases of insomnia, massage and going for walks. He further recommends strengthening the patients' reasoning powers by asking them questions or getting them to read and criticize texts which contain false statements. Apart from this the patients should spend their time in light reading, play acting (the plays should be in a spirit contrary to the patients' mental states) or delivering speeches to a friendly audience. The tasks allotted to patients should be selected according to their previous education. Chess and travel are also recommended. These methods in large measure can be traced back at least to Asclepiades (c. 100 B.C.) . The patient should be treated energetically in the acute stages of the illness, gently during remissions. Soranus makes use of hellebore as an emetic. However, he rejects a large number of therapeutic measures among them darkness, starvation, continuous fettering, opium, excessive blood-letting, enemata, alcohol, whipping, music and love.

The chapter on melancholia is appreciably shorter. Soranus is a methodist and believes in a solidist pathology. He does not see melancholia as black bile but as "black rage." He considers that it occurs most commonly in men at the prime of life and that it can be caused by digestive upsets, drugs, fear and grief. The main symptoms are depression, mutism, death wishes, marked suspiciousness, weeping, muttering and occasional joviality. Melancholia is not a form of mania. The latter is a disease of the head, while melancholia is a disease of the oesophagus. Treatment is the same as for mania except that local measures should be directed not at the head but at the regions of the stomach and shoulder blades. Soranus advises against the use of hellebore, blood-letting and excessively powerful drugs.

Summarizing his views and comparing them with those of others, we can say that Soranus, like Celsus and Aretaeus, recognized three main mental diseases: phrenitis, mania and melancholia. He did not even mention hysteria which was described by Aretaeus. It should be noted that on one occasion the latter mentioned senile dementia in passing. All three writers were extreme somaticists. The body-mind dualism which predominated among Greek philosophers was to them an alien concept. Their analysis and general treatment of the three mental diseases is based on the assumption that they are dealing with physical illnesses. Only homosexuality is regarded by Soranus as an illness of the psyche. Aretaeus thought that hysteria was a disease of the uterus (wandering of the uterus) and went so far as to deal with it alongside fatal uterine haemorrhages and inflammations. Despite this he recognized that the same disease picture could occur in men. He too allowed clinical observation to triumph over theoretical considerations.

Although mental diseases were regarded as physical illnesses, the brain was rarely mentioned. This is not surprising, since the ancient Greeks were grossly deficient in their concepts both of the functions of this organ and of the peripheral nerves. The emphasis put on phrenitis may have been partly a subjective one and partly due to the predominance of febrile illnesses, or to misdiagnosis, since fever was diagnosed only by hand. Aretaeus incidentally pointed out the interesting difference that while in phrenitis perception itself was disturbed, in melancholia and mania what was perceived was wrongly interpreted.

Neither mania nor melancholia can be recognized in any of our present-day syndromes. Mania simply meant an agitated form of insanity, melancholia a quiet one. Aretaeus's view that melancholia may pass into mania can, therefore, only with some qualifications be regarded as foreshadowing manic-depressive psychosis. His theory that melancholia was generally limited to a single "phantasy" was frequently put forward in later years.

In contrast to Greek tradition in general, Soranus did not discuss prognosis in mental diseases. Aretaeus however stressed the frequency of relapses, and the fact that these illnesses were in practice often of lifelong duration and that they frequently terminated in states of silliness or of paralysis (!). Because mental illnesses were often incurable, the physician was thought to have the moral right to refuse to undertake treatment. This right incidentally was accorded to the medical profession until the end of the eighteenth century.

Soranus's treatment consisted essentially of isolation, moderate blood-letting, diet, massage, and local treatments applied to the head and the oesophagus. In complete contrast to his basic assumptions, he also made use of psychotherapy. Celsus and Aretaeus held very different theories about the nature of mental illness and the seat of the soul. Their descriptions however of these diseases and their treatment closely resembled those of Soranus, with the difference that as humoral pathologists, they laid greater stress on blood-letting and the use of cathartics and drugs in general. Celsus was also a great deal more ruthless. His "psychotherapy" includes measures such as menaces, torture, whipping, and sudden, brutal ducking. Jean Starobinski (*Histoire du Traitement de la Mélancholie des Origines à 1900,* Basle, 1960) has correctly pointed out that a whole series of ancient philosophical treatises, for example those of Seneca, can be described as psychotherapeutic writings. Again we have no information as to where the mentally ill were housed. Some Roman archives suggest that they were accommodated in prisons; but this whole problem was still relegated to the vast area of private concern and hospitals did not exist at all.

Greek psychiatry presents us with the first clinical observations and with the first attempts at a classification of mental illnesses. It was never a slave to its own theories. Treatment was essentially physical, sometimes psychological, and always empirical. Although its successes did not measure up to those in other branches of Greek medicine, it is still of considerable importance, particularly when one considers subsequent achievements in psychiatry.

CHAPTER III

THE MIDDLE AGES AND RENAISSANCE

THERE is not much to say about mediaeval psychiatry, partly because we know very little about mediaeval medicine in general, partly because, in contrast to other fields, there were few positive developments in medicine during the Middle Ages. On the contrary, much occurred that was harmful such as the fragmentation of medicine. Surgery fell into the hands of barbers and their assistants, obstetrics into those of ignorant midwives, and psychiatry was practiced by exorcising priests and witch hunting clerics.

Here and there physicians attempted with more or less success to preserve the Greek traditions of psychiatry. This was clearly shown by Temkin in the special case of epilepsy.[1] The classical naturalistic concepts of mental illness were thus after all preserved in a few places and among some sections of society.

This was particularly true within the hospitals which were the greatest medical achievement of the Middle Ages. Although we know that large hospitals were established as early as the fourth century, we have details about psychiatric sections in such institutions only since the founding of the great Arabic hospitals (Baghdad, 750; Cairo, 873. The Arabs also accommodated the mentally ill in monasteries.) To this day the Mohammedans have unusually sympathetic attitudes to the mentally ill which are reflected in the Koran. The Arabs were also apparently the first to build special institutions for the insane: Damascus, 800; Aleppo, 1270; Kaladun, 1283; Cairo, 1304; Fez, 1500. The Arabs achieved more in the care of the insane than in the field of psychiatry itself. Here, as in the

---

[1] Temkin, O., *The Falling Sickness*, Baltimore, 1945. Whitwell, J. R., *Historical Notes on Psychiatry*, London, 1936, contains translations of several mediaeval physicians. See also Wright, E. H., *Mediaeval Attitudes towards Mental Sickness*, Bull. Hist. Med. 7: 352, 1939.

rest of medicine, they merely repeated and expanded the Greek concepts of mental illness.

Psychiatric departments in general hospitals were not rare in the Middle Ages. They existed in the west since the thirteenth century, e.g. in Paris, Lyon, Montpellier, London, Munich, Braunschweig, Freiburg, Zurich, Basle etc. Here the classical traditions undoubtedly survived.

On the whole, however, what little knowledge the Greeks had established was lost and a tragic decline to an earlier cultural level ensued. The clock was put back by a thousand years. For over a thousand years the mentally ill were again regarded as possessed by the devil and by evil spirits, or were considered to be witches or sorcerers who could produce the illness in others. "Apparitions" and hallucinations were thought of as the work of the devil. It followed as a consequence that the physician was excluded from the field of mental illness whose study was taken over by the Inquisitors. In the Middle Ages one must go to the handbooks and protocols of witch hunters and exorcists for descriptions of the mentally ill; they are not found in the medical books of the period. Psychiatrically the Middle Ages are also remarkable for the frequency of psychic epidemics or mass psychoses such as the flagellationist movement, dancing mania, children's crusades, Jew baiting and "possession" of whole communities of people, especially in monasteries.[2] On the other hand, it must not be forgotten that some mediaeval institutions, such as monasteries and pilgrimages were often sources of refuge and support for mentally ill individuals, and it is quite possible that occasionally exorcism was in fact therapeutic.

The decline of psychiatry did not end with the brilliant period of the Renaissance and the beginning of the modern era. On the contrary, it was at this time that the lunacy of the sane reached its zenith. During the whole of the Middle Ages, although many devils were exorcised, the number of witches executed was probably nowhere near the number burned at the stake during the relatively enlightened fifteenth century and the subsequent two hundred years. The *Malleus Maleficarum,* the infamous handbook of the witch hunters, which was written by the Dominicans Heinrich Kraemer and Jakob Sprenger, appeared as late as 1486. It shows

---

[2] Calmeil, L. F., *De la folie considerée sous le rapport pathologique, historique et judiciaire,* Paris, 1845.

clearly that not only the possessed but also a large number of witches were in fact mentally ill. The most renowned physicians of the Renaissance, men such as Fernel, Paré and Johannes Lange, were among the most ardent believers in this barbarous nonsense.[3]

A small elite of outstanding medical men however emerged during the Renaissance who made new and honorable contributions to psychiatry. They declared that many possessed and many witches had nothing whatever to do with the devil or with other supernatural forces but had become mentally ill for very natural reasons and merited medical attention and not the stake. They thus publicly expressed opinions which, according to the polemics of the *Malleus Maleficarum,* had been whispered among the "Heretics." Although the words and deeds of Cornelius Agrippa, Della Porta, Cardano, Paracelsus, Lemnius, Reginald Scotus and Johannes Weyer retain certain mediaeval characteristics, they fully merit the high-flown title of "The first psychiatric revolution" bestowed on them by Zilboorg. Other men, like Gesner, Montanus, Benedictus and Schenck von Grafenberg, reported cases of mental disease and their treatment by natural means without discussing "possession" as such.

Both the increase of witch hunting and the beginning of scientific protest are aspects of the Renaissance which can probably be attributed to the same basic phenomenon: namely the moral-ideological and politico-economic disintegration of mediaeval society. This stimulated and encouraged a few great minds towards an increased freedom of thought but filled the majority with panic and anxiety. It provoked the upholders of the old system to irrational counterattacks on the devil and his handymen, and the almost unendurable celibacy of the Inquisitors added its particular misogynous flavor to this movement. On the basis of the *Malleus Maleficarum* everyone who showed the slightest psychological deviation or peculiarity was regarded as a witch or sorcerer. Not only mental illness but almost any affliction of the body (impotence, sterility, deformity, infant mortality) and all of life's misfortunes (a poor harvest, death, a broken marriage) were regarded as the works of the devil.

It would be wrong however, to think of the psychiatric revolution as a modern movement. The men responsible were children of their

---

[3] To avoid misplaced optimism, it is unfortunately necessary to point out that similar irrational and paranoid ideas can be found even in the twentieth century, although here they usually appear in the guise of "naturalism" rather than of the supernatural.

time. They did not leap into a new era but merely took a step forward. But even this was enough to draw upon them hatred and persecution from their contemporaries and to earn them the gratitude and admiration of later generations. Among the writings of this new "school of psychiatry" most animosity was aroused by the book of Johannes Weyer of Brabant (1515-1588), called "De Praestigiis Daemonum," which appeared in 1563. Weyer[4] begins with a description of the devil, his attributes and his cohorts. The power of the devil like that of witches is he says limited by God, and as a non-corporeal being the devil is unable to engage in many activities with which he has been credited such as, for example, sexual intercourse. Weyer remarks that natural events are often regarded as works of the devil. He believes not only in the devil but also in so-called evil magicians such as Arnald of Villanova, Roger Bacon and Faust. He demands their punishment and excepts only his teacher, Cornelius Agrippa, who, according to Weyer, did not belong to their group.

Next he turns to witches. It is obvious to him that the phenomena described by witches are not real (and hence not punishable) but are phantasies instilled into them by the devil. His work is made easy in their case since witches are generally people with melancholic mental illnesses who are recognized to be prone to disturbances of the imagination. Moreover, it would be blasphemous to look on the activities of witches as real, because one would then be attributing to them and to the devil powers which God alone possesses. Occasionally the phantasies of witches can be traced to the use of belladonna ointments, and here Weyer refers to the experiments of Della Porta and Cardano with such ointments. Magic, he says, is not in fact efficacious and it would be better to treat witches with sympathy. The tests to which they are submitted are senseless. The foreign bodies, such as nails, knives, etc., which they vomit up are not products of their own bodies but have been introduced into them by the devil. Sometimes these objects can have a natural origin. Impotence, he says, is due to natural causes. Lycanthropy (the belief of having been changed into a wolf), is not due to witchcraft but to madness. Somewhere else, however, Weyer states that this is an illusion attributable to the work of the devil.

[4] Johannes Weyer (Wierus): born 1515 in Grave, North Brabant; studied in Bonn, Paris and Orleans; 1545, city medical officer of Arnheim; 1550-1578, private physician to Duke William of Jülich-Cleve-Berg; died 1588.

The possessed are either mentally ill people suffering from melancholia or charlatans with a great desire to feel important. Weyer was particularly clever at exposing such frauds.

In the treatment of the possessed, he says, the priests have turned religion into magic. Their methods of treatment are successful because they act on the imagination. In cases of possession a doctor should be called in first. His purges can sometimes be beneficial, even in the case of illness due to supernatural causes. Subsequently one should send the patient to a priest for a kind of re-education.

These, briefly, are the opinions defended by Weyer in his *"De Praestigiis Daemonum."* They are a mixture of traditional views, theological criticism and original clinical observations. In other fields also Weyer was a very able clinician. I think it would be a mistake to assume, as has so often been done, that Weyer was hypocritical and in fact no longer believed in any supernatural causes for disease. There is no evidence for this. On the contrary, it is much more likely and more natural that Weyer still believed in the devil and in evil magicians. But that is not the most important part of his work. The important part is that he recognized the witches and the possessed as mentally ill and demanded that they should be treated by the doctor and not the priest. Weyer is neither the first nor the only representative of such views. He himself had heard them from his teacher, Cornelius Agrippa, and could find them in the writings of Della Porta, Cardano, Andrea a Laguna, Amatus Lusitanus and Paracelsus. But he was their most explicit, most forceful and most successful champion.

The Renaissance is an age of profound contradictions. Side by side with the ruthless persecution of the insane as witches we find everywhere signs of a deep sympathy for the unfortunate sick. This diversity of attitudes found expression not only in the writings of the authors cited above but also in the creation of numerous institutions for the insane. This was particularly the case in Spain, which then experienced a "golden era" of medicine and of civilization in general, and where Arabian influences were felt most strongly. Institutions for the mentally ill were opened in Valencia in 1409; Saragossa, 1425; Seville and Valladolid, 1436; and in Toledo in 1480. It is characteristic of the period that some few decades later the repentant veteran soldier, Bernadino Alvarez, built a similar hospital (San Hippolyto) in newly conquered Mexico. This was the first of its kind on the American continent. A sympathetic understanding for the mentally ill is also strongly expressed in the writings of the Spanish humanist, Juan Louis Vives (1492-1540). The opening of special institutions in Spain was followed in the 16th century by the founding of similar hospitals in Rome, Paris, Amsterdam, Marseilles, Avignon, Hamburg, Lubeck and elsewhere. It is questionable whether the 14th century German mad houses (Elbing, Hamburg, Nurenberg) can be regarded as belonging to the same category.[5]

The significance of the Renaissance for psychiatry goes further than the rebirth of a humane attitude towards the insane. Doubts as to the supernatural causation of mental illness and other phenomena such as miracles which had previously been explained on this basis, led to a search for natural forces and natural causes; and we now find the concept of "imaginatio," for example, in the writings of the above-mentioned authors as well as in those of Pomponatius, Libavius and Pico della Mirandola. This imaginatio is very similar to our present-day concept of suggestion. It is a force capable of causing both physical and psychological illnesses and also of curing them. Since we ourselves are not very clear as to what exactly we mean by suggestion, we should not be too critical of the sixteenth century workers if they also remained somewhat vague as to the exact nature of their imaginatio.

Whatever one's opinion of Paracelsus,[6] he was undoubtedly the most renowned physician of his time and for this reason alone he merits our attention. He was also much more concerned with psychiatry than his contemporaries. In about 1520 he wrote a small book called *"Diseases which lead to a Loss of Reason"* which was published in 1567. In his introductory remarks he makes it quite

---

5 Ackerknecht, E. H. and Akert, K., *Wechselnde Formen der Unterbringung von Geisteskranken*, Schweiz. Med. Wschrift., 94: 1541-1546, 1964.

6 Phillipus Aureolus Theophratus Bombastus von Hohenheim, called Paracelsus: Born 1491 in Maria Einsiedeln, son of a doctor. 1502, moved with his father to Villach in Carinthia, Austria, seat of the mines of the Fugger family. Early contact there with alchemy. From 1507, wandering scholar; Tuebingen, Heidelberg, Freiburg, Cologne, Erfurt, Vienna. 1513, Ferrara, where he is said to have taken a degree. Army surgeon in Italy, Holland, Sweden. Also travelled in Spain, Portugal, France, England, Russia, Turkey, Egypt and the Balkans. 1524, attempted to settle in Salzburg but failed because of the peasant wars. 1526, Professor at Basle but 1528 had to flee from there. Continued a life of wandering in Southern Germany, Switzerland, Bohemia and Austria. 1532, religious crisis. Died in Salzburg, 1541.

clear that whatever the clerics might say, mental illnesses are not caused by spirits but are natural diseases. This was a courageous and extremely valuable statement to make in his day. Although his writings abound in Greek, Roman and Arabic ideas, Paracelsus was concerned to build up a new system of medicine and he created a new classification of mental diseases in place of the classical triad of mania, melancholia and phrenitis. He distinguished the following mental illnesses: epilepsy, mania, "true insanity," St. Vitus dance and suffocatio intellectus (the old hysteria).

He described five types of epilepsy: that arising from the brain, the liver, the heart, the intestines and the limbs. This was not an unusual concept for his time. His clinical description (fainting, seizures, sudden or gradual falling, frothing and occasionally incontinence of urine) shows that he did not clearly differentiate between epilepsy and hysteria. Epilepsy, according to him, could occur in any living thing, not only in lions and squirrels, but also in trees. It was a disturbance of the spiritus vitae, precipitated by food or "vapours." In accord with his philosophy of the macrocosmos-microcosmos he likened it to an earthquake. The illness he said began as early as intra-uterine life and consisted first and foremost of seething of the spiritus vitae in the various organs of its origin.

Mania he said consisted of a disturbance of reason and not of the senses. Its manifestations were excited and unreasonable behavior, agitation and irritability. There was a tendency to relapse and the illness could be primary, occurring in physically healthy persons, or it could be secondary to other diseases. A substance whose vapours rose to the brain was distilled either above or below the diaphragm. If this substance originated from excreta, the patients would refuse food, would talk to themselves, would be given to vomiting and would ignore their surroundings. If it were distilled in the limbs, they would be cheerful, wild and excited. If the temperature were high, the humor vitae would burn, its finer particles would be separated off and would rise upwards. The substance at times coagulated in the head and might change into worms; at other times it would lead to the formation of ulcers. (The spontaneous generation of worms was not questioned until the seventeenth century.) Paracelsus naturally disputed the theory of the four temperaments and the four humors. Mania, he said, arose from the spiritus vitae alone. It exposed secret "attitudes and qualities" in the afflicted persons which until then had been latent.

True insanity ("those who are really mad") he described as a permanent state related to the stars. He distinguished five sub-groups: lunatici, insani, vesani, melancholici and obsessi. The first four, he said, had nothing to do with the devil, for where there is no reason, the devil has lost his rights. Such patients do not suffer pain as do those afflicted with mania, chorea lasciva, suffocatio intellectus or epilepsy. In the case of lunatici, the spiritus vitae is under the invisible influence of the moon and the stars, just as iron is influenced by a magnet or as water is drawn from the earth by the sun. The insani are born mad (this was a new point of view) either because the semen was diseased or because they were affected by the moon in utero. The vesani are poisoned with food or drink, particularly with food which has been subjected to the magic of love. Some patients think of nothing but love, some only of war, and yet others of climbing and running.

"St. Vitus dance" (dancing mania) could not, according to him, be attributed to the saints, since these do not cause diseases. He suggested chorea lasciva as a more appropriate name for it and said it was due either to the precipitation of certain irritating salts in the veins of laughter by the spiritus vitae or to imaginatio (imagination and imitation). The St. Vitus dance of Paracelsus' day is not to be equated with our chorea, but with dancing mania which indeed showed many sexual features.

His suffocatio intellectus again appears to be a combination of epilepsy and hysteria. He described it as a natural disease due either to intestinal worms, intra-uterine events, over-eating or excessive sleeping. Intestinal worms were still regarded as the main cause of mental illnesses by the well known Paris pathologist, Prost, at the beginning of the nineteenth century. Again, according to Paracelsus, the illness was due to fumes from the affected organs reaching the head or being sucked into the heart. Pressure in these organs could cause tremors, seizures and sometimes death. The illnesses could also be precipitated by blows to the head. Paracelsus mentions head injuries so frequently as a cause of seizures and insanity that one can regard him as a forerunner of J. H. Jackson.

Only brief mention will be made of the chapters on therapy in Paracelsus's *"Diseases which lead to a Loss of Reason."* They are remarkable for the absence of any mention of psychotherapy and

St. Vitus cures possession
(Swabian painting XIIth century)

JOHN WEYER

for their emphasis on chemical measures. In the case of epilepsy, Paracelsus departs from his principle that physical ailments should be treated only by physical means, "spiritual" ailments by "spiritual" means, by suggesting that the "spiritual" affliction of epilepsy be treated with physical drugs such as camphor, powdered unicorn, etc. He goes on to list a number of "spiritual" medicaments whose effect was coagulating, astringent or specific. All illnesses, he said, were curable with his Arcana, which were manufactured not by physicians but by "artists" (the alchemists). Some of his recipes for Arcana, like Hungarian vitriol or oil of Arcani, contain camphor, skull shavings, unicorn, herbs and root plants. In the treatment of mania one should allow the vapors to escape by opening up those parts of the body to which mania rises (toes, fingers, head). He also recommends cooling and astringent measures to combat the dangerous vapors. In cases of lunatici one has to counteract the magnetic forces of the moon and sun by such means as his so-called quintessences, in particular his "quinta essentia auri." Congenital madness should be prevented by means of "coitus artificialis" between the parents and by means of drugs. Vesani are treated with what he calls specific drugs, with sedativa and with remedies which strengthen the spiritus vitae.

In the case of chorea lasciva due to excessive rage, the patient was advised to let out all his oaths on a waxen image and subsequently to burn this. If chorea lasciva is due to sexual phantasies, Paracelsus recommends confinement in a dark cell, fasting, "a good stick" and ducking in cold water. These measures can, of course, be regarded as a form of psychotherapy although Paracelsus explained their effects solely on a physical basis. For chorea originating in the laughing veins he recommends aurum potabile, ointments,, etc. For suffocatio he prescribes antihelminthics, laxatives, fumigation, ointments and other drugs.

From a study of this work one gains the impression that Paracelsus was a chemical somaticist with occasional psychological and clinical insights (like that of the sexual rather than uterine nature of hysterical seizures). He describes the body as if it were a kind of alchemist's kitchen in which caustic fumes rise up to cause mental illnesses. This is in no way surprising since Paracelsus's main contribution to medicine was the introduction of chemical concepts. Neither is it surprising to find that his treatment is not psychotherapeutic but primarily chemical. The astrological references in his book are in full harmony with the fashion of his time in which most scholars held astrology to be a serious science. Despite its occasional references to magic, his book is essentially naturalistic and Paracelsus' new classification of mental diseases is probably no worse than those of his predecessors. His therapeutic optimism is great and at times comes very near to quackery.

If this were all we knew about the psychiatry of Paracelsus it would be relatively simple to see it in perspective and to evaluate it as a whole. Unfortunately, however, there is another book by Paracelsus about mental illnesses, called *"The Invisible Diseases"* and written in 1531. In this book chemistry and clinical symptoms are suddenly forgotten, unless we choose to interpret as such his remarks about the influence of the imagination of pregnant women on the formation of the foetus, or his statement that those who kill themselves in despair are inspired by the devil. We now learn that St. Vitus dance, St. Anthony's fire and other such diseases are due to "faith." This book is the work of a mystical philosopher and can be so variously interpreted that every idea entering a physician's head then, now, or in the future, can be read into it or picked out from it without anyone ever being sure what the author really meant.

Furthermore, we find in Paracelsus's *"De Generatione Stultorum"* the first mention of the relationship between goitre and cretinism and a truly moving appeal for the understanding and humane treatment of "fools." At the same time, however, we find in his *"De Lunaticis"* (Strebel Edition, Vol. 2, pages 127-129) the statements that madness can be avoided by means of confession and that the afflicted should be burned to prevent their becoming tools of the devil. We also find a complete treatise on those possessed by the devil who are not amenable to medical treatment but can only be cured through the power of Christ, by prayer and by fasting. Paracelsus also wrote a book about witches in which he tells us that they are responsible for thunder storms and produce disease by shooting foreign bodies under the skin (if Australian medicine men had been literate, one of them could have written this chapter). They also induce impotence and congenital malformations. Furthermore we learn that witches are born as such and can be recognized by the following infallible signs: a curved nose, avoidance of sexual intercourse, especially in the widowed state, or an inclination for intercourse on Saturdays, Fridays and Thursdays.

Paracelsus ends with an appeal in favor of "saving" rather than burning the witches. With these humane and laudable sentiments one can only agree, although they are neither particularly medical nor psychiatric. One can of course take these incredible contradictions in Paracelsus' work as signs of his greatness and depth of understanding. This has often been done. It seems to me, however, that there is a simpler and more obvious explanation, namely that he was a muddled and illogical writer. As a campaigner against ancient dogmas and an unprejudiced observer and chemist, Paracelsus undoubtedly stood at the cradle of modern medicine and psychiatry. But he was also a mediaeval mystic and an immensely inconsistent confabulator. As such he often supported the forces of reaction and caused a great deal of confusion.

CHAPTER IV

SEVENTEENTH CENTURY PSYCHIATRY

YET another Swiss, Felix Plater (1536-1614), distinguished himself at the beginning of the seventeenth century by his enquiries into the nature of mental disorders along the lines of the Greek model. At the very beginning of his "Medical Practice" he devotes several chapters (150 pages in all) to this subject and his companion volume of clinical observations contains accounts of many interesting cases of mental illness. Plater appears to have had a strong personal interest in the insane and often allowed himself to be locked in with them in their cells. He classifies mental diseases into: (1) imbecilitas; (2) consternatio, which term he uses to describe both the stupor of febrile delirium as well as catatonic states (flexibilitas cerea); his stupor cases include one of great interest in which a brain tumor was found at post mortem. Plater was one of the campaigners for the use of autopsy to illuminate clinical experience; (3) alienato, which he divides into dementia; alcoholism, which he also discusses under the heading of imbecilitas and consternatio (following the discovery of distilling processes in the Middle Ages we now begin to hear much more about alcoholism); love and jealousy; melancholia and hypochondriasis; and possession by the devil! Under alienatio he also includes raving mania, St. Vitus dance and phrenitis; (4) defatigatio, whose main manifestation is insomnia, is due to purely supernatural agents (God or the devil) and can, he says, only be treated by corresponding measures. Despite his superstitious prejudices, however, Plater surpassed all his predecessors in the accuracy of his clinical observations. Robert Burton's *"Anatomy of Melancholy"* also appeared for the first time in 1624. This work, which was to become so extremely popular, was in fact simply a collection of classical material, written in the spirit of the times and possessed of certain literary merits. A special form of insanity, dependent upon climate and found particularly among the

Swiss, was described in the seventeenth century by J. J. Harder (1678) and J. Hofer (1685) of Basle under the name of "nostalgia" (home sickness).

The magnificent developments of psychiatry in the sixteenth century were not on the whole followed by steady progress in the next. On the contrary they faded out. Although the belief in witches declined during the seventeenth century, it still claimed numerous victims and in France the death penalty for witches was not abolished until 1680. But no sooner had the mentally ill escaped odium as the devil's associates, than they were dismissed as "asocial" and treated accordingly.

The absolutist governments of the mid-seventeenth century decided to resolve their social crisis by incarcerating all the poor.[1a] In Paris this "renfermement des pauvres" occurred in May 1657. The men were taken to the Bicêtre, the women to the Salpêtrière. In France these pauper prisons were deceitfully called "Hôpital genéral"; in Germany, more truthfully, "Zuchthaus"; in Great Britain "workhouse." In them beggars and vagrants were confined together with cripples, old people, orphans, prostitutes, those afflicted with venereal disease, homosexuals, "unbelievers," criminals and the insane. The latter were so numerous that special departments had to be set aside for them. While previously the insane were only rarely kept in prisons, this became the rule under the absolutist governments of the day. Little wonder that in these institutions the mentally ill too were chained and that doctors practically never consulted. The prison section of the Salpêtrière was abolished only in 1795; that of the Bicêtre not until 1836. In 1828 the number of mentally ill patients in English "workhouses" was still 9,000.

Less barbarous, religious private institutions, such as St. Lazare in Paris, were founded by St. Vincent de Paul, a staunch campaigner for the humane treatment of the insane. Even these, however, combined the functions of a prison with those of a mental hospital and did not remove the stigma of social ostracism from the insane.

While the psychoses thus continued to elude the influences of medicine in the seventeenth century, much attention was devoted to another group of mental disorders: the neuroses. Neurotics, after

---

[1a] Foucault, M., *Folie et Raison*, Paris, 1961. Rosen, G., *Social Attitudes to Madness in 17th Century Europe*, Journ. Hist. Med. 18: 220, 1963.

all, walk about freely and appear in large numbers in the doctor's consulting room. The psychiatry of the neuroses could accurately be called "out-patient psychiatry." As soon as doctors began to study these illnesses more closely, they seemed impressed with the idea that neuroses were becoming more common. As early as 1600, G. Mercuriali (1530-1606) complained of the increase of hypochondriasis. Thomas Sydenham, the great English clinician (1621-1689), of whom much more will be said later, was of the opinion that half of his non-febrile patients, that is, a sixth of his total practice, were hysterical. In the eighteenth century George Cheyne (1671-1743), an English clinician, believed that a third of all his patients were neurotic. He actually called his book, published in 1733, the *"English Disease"* and was of the opinion that the English were particularly nervous!

Finally, in the early nineteenth century Thomas Trotter (1761-1832) in his "View of the Nervous Temperament" declared that two-thirds of all his patients were neurotic. Trotter had also written a book on alcoholism, a subject which preoccupied people increasingly. From Sydenham onwards the belief gained strength that all the diverse symptoms and "diseases" which were called hysterical, hypochondriacal and, later, nervous, were manifestations of some hidden malady but that this was not a disease of the uterus as had previously been thought. Thus we find a remarkable similarity in the books of Sydenham, Cheyne, Pomme, Trotter, Whytt and in those of Brachet, Dubois and Louyer-Villermay up to George Miller Beard's work on neurasthenia (1880). All attempted to collect together the many, varied symptoms and to find a common cause for them in the light of the current trends of their respective periods.

It seems desirable to present a short abstract of Sydenham's[1] famous notes on hysteria (1680 letter to Dr. Cole), the first, and by no means the worst, of the writings on the neuroses which succeeded one another without interruption until the late nineteenth century.

---

[1] Thomas Sydenham, born 1624 at Wynfort Eagle, Dorsetshire, England, of a Puritan family. Father and brother, like himself, were officers in Cromwell's army. 1642, began his studies at Oxford University, but joined the army and returned 1647; 1650 again joined the army; 1656 married and started practising in London; 1659-1661 in Montpellier. Only in 1663 was he made licentiate of the Royal College of Physicians (aged 39). Escaped from the plague in 1665 and wrote his first book on fever, which he dedicated to Robert Boyle and which had an introductory poem by his friend, John Locke. Died of gout in 1689.

Sydenham regarded hysteria as a most widespread and puzzling disease whose treatment presented the utmost difficulty. According to him it occurred mainly in women and spared only those women who lead a hard life. Men could also be afflicted and, in particular, those addicted to a sedentary life. In the case of men the illness was usually called hypochondriasis but it was, in fact, the same as hysteria. The main feature of hysteria was the variety of forms which it could take. Diagnostic errors were easily made. It could stimulate apoplexy if it occurred after labor or after great excitement. It could take the form of epilepsy, headache, palpitations, cough, "passio iliaca" (chronic appendicitis) ; of renal colic, diarrhoea, of pain and swelling of muscle; of toothache or backache; of cold in the presence of a normal pulse (the pulse, according to him, remained normal even in cases of hysterical colic or vomiting) , and of a feeling of annihilation in the chest. Sydenham (and many of his followers) laid great stress on the production of large amounts of clear urine as a symptom of hysteria. He described hysterics as often being depressed, often however boisterous and in general very labile. They always retained their reason. The forms which hysteria could take were so manifold that he considered it impossible to list them all.

Hysteria could be precipitated by excitement; also by prolonged fasting or severe blood-letting or purgation. It was due to "ataxia" or "spasmus" of the "spiritus animales" to which Galen and Paracelsus had introduced us. It is interesting to see how Sydenham attempted, in the language of his day, to explain that the illness seemed to him neither purely physical nor purely psychological. Whilst according to Hippocratic tradition he attributed other diseases to the humors, he made an exception in the case of hysteria and called this a disease of the spiritus animales. Women, he said, were more often affected because they were weaker and because their "spiritus" was more delicate. Among Sydenham's many interesting case histories is a most impressive one of a nobleman who suffered from hysterical attacks of weeping.

Sydenham's treatment was simple: he used phlebotomy and purging less often than usual and relied above all on iron preparations, and also on milk diets and on horse-riding which the old cavalry officer held in very high regard. He attempted to suppress attacks by the use of the old, evil-smelling drugs which Aretaeus had already recommended, although for different reasons. He prescribed opium for pain although he was aware of the risk of addiction.

Sydenham's concepts of hysteria, like many other of his ideas, were as Isler[2] has shown, strongly influenced by Thomas Willis whose immence importance we are only gradually rediscovering now. Sydenham did not however accept Willis' idea that hysteria is an illness of the brain rather than the uterus (a notion voiced by Charles Le Pois as long ago as 1618). Despite Willis the superstitious belief that hysteria originated in the womb persisted into the nineteenth century.

Until recently Willis was remembered in the history of psychiatry only for his advocacy of brutal treatment methods. These he limited however to patients with chronic mania. In other cases he recommended a change of scene, working on the land, mathematics, etc. The writings of Vinchon, Cranefield and others have drawn our attention to his excellent observations of mental deficiency, epilepsy and of schizophrenia-like and manic-depressive mood states. He was one of the first to describe Progressive Paralysis and his psychologicaly theories were very influential.

Above all we must recognize Willis as the father of Neurology. The century in which the neuroses were first explored also gave birth to neurology. Willis' achievements in the field of neuroanatomy (his descriptions of the cranial nerves and of the autonomic nervous system) match his discoveries in neurophysiology (the reflex—he is the originator of both the concept and the word; cerebro-cortical functioning and cerebral localization; inner secretions) and in neuropathology (the first description of myasthenia gravis).

Another significant work was the book on medical jurisprudence: *Questiones medico legales,* written by Paolo Zachias (1584-1659), the pope's physician which dealt with a number of psychiatric problems.[3] Although Zachias retained many of the traditional errors,

[2] Isler, H. R., *Thomas Willis,* Stuttgart, 1965. Thomas Willis, born near Oxford 1621, died in London 1675. He studied at Oxford, went into practice there in 1646, and in 1660 his Royalism earned him the chair of Natural History. In 1666 he moved to London where up to his death he was actively engaged in research, writing and an enormous private practice.

[3] Ackerknecht, E. H., *Early History of Legal Medicine,* Ciba Symposia 11: 1286-1316, 1950/51.

he shows a great deal of commonsense in his discussion of such topics as possession, malingering and impotence.

It must also be mentioned that blood transfusion, one of the widely practised treatment methods of today, was introduced in the seventeenth century, more or less as a psychiatric treatment method. The Parisian Professor Jean Denis transferred appreciable amounts of arterial blood from lambs to the veins of mental patients, at first with some success (? due to the effect of shock). Subsequent fatalities led to the prohibition of this procedure. It lay dormant until the surgeons revived it in the nineteenth century and was not successfully applied until the discovery of blood groups by Landsteiner in the twentieth century made its wider use possible.

CHAPTER V

EIGHTEENTH CENTURY PSYCHIATRY

In the eighteenth century psychiatry at last reached the status of an independent science. Psychiatric achievements surpassed earlier efforts, at first in quantity and later also in quality. This was not primarily due only to developments in medicine but to the philosophy of enlightenment which pervaded the whole century. With the spread of enlightenment, belief in possession by evil spirits became just one more manifestation of the detested enemy "superstition" and (with the exception of a few setbacks among the German Romantics of the first half of the nineteenth century) it was now destroyed once and for all. Since the concept of the immortal soul was of no importance in this philosophical system, mental disorders could be viewed as disorders of the mortal brain or thinking apparatus and as such could now at last be studied on a scientific basis. At the same time it became possible to give up a purely somatic viewpoint and to introduce psychology deliberately into psychiatry. Cartesian philosophy, no doubt, played a part in this development.

The growth and development of psychiatry in the eighteenth century was greatly influenced by the deeply philanthropic interests of the philosophers of enlightenment. As reason was their highest good, how they sympathized with those who had lost reason! Their optimism was boundless; as was their belief in attaining human perfection. Thus they overcame the fatalist belief in the incurability of insanity; they founded numerous institutions for the mentally sick, and improved the regime within these institutions until the day when, through the great symbolic gesture of taking off the chains of the "mad men," these were definitely reinstated as human beings.

This decisive advance occurred at the end of the century when Abraham Joly in Geneva (1787) ; Pinel in the Paris Bicêtre (1793) ; William Tuke, the Quaker, of York (1796) ; Vincenzo Chiarugi (1759-1820) after 1788 in Tuscany, and John Gottfried Langermann (1768-1852) in 1805 in Bayreuth, struck off the chains from the insane. The prolonged and intensive preoccupation with psychiatry which went on during the whole of the eighteenth century had, of course, prepared the way and provided a basis for this event. As psychiatry was now mainly practised in asylums which were still outside the universities, the centre of interest shifted once more from the neuroses to the psychoses.

The eighteenth century saw the creation of numerous asylums which continued into the nineteenth century and which provided the material structure for the future development of psychiatry. We shall mention only a few: Bologna (1710); Warsaw (1726); Berlin (1728); Dublin (1745); Ludwigsburg (1746); London (1759); Deventer (1760); Manchester and Copenhagen (1766); Williamsburg (1773); Vienna (1784); Frankfurt on Main (1785).

The movement of enlightenment also enabled psychiatrists to demand the right to be heard in the courts. Another result was the new and strong interest taken in the prophylaxis of mental disease. This particular interest was shown by the movement of enlightenment in all fields of medicine and therefore also in psychiatry. Enlightenment is after all the mother of the social sciences and their application to medicine. The term "sciences sociales" appears for the first time in the *Encyclopédie* of Diderot and d'Alembert and it is not surprising that in the eighteenth century we come across the first sociological theories about the causes of mental illness. The men of the enlightenment also developed an understandable enthusiasm for the study of alcoholism, which is after all a preventable and curable disease with profound social causes and consequences. Among workers in this field were Hales, Lettsom, Benjamin Rush and Trotter, to mention only a few. Trotter quite specifically called alcohol addiction a mental illness. J. P. Frank talks of a decrease of alcoholism in Germany as a result of the movement of enlightenment.

The decisive turning point was no doubt due to the influence of George Ernst Stahl[1] (1660-1734), the clinician and chemist of Halle.

---

[1] George Ernst Stahl, born 1660 at Ansbach. After 1694 Professor at the newly-founded university of Halle together with his friend and later rival Friedrich Hoffman. 1716, came to Berlin as personal physician to the King of Prussia. Said to have died there in a state of mental confusion in 1734. He was a pietist, invented "animism" in the field of medicine, and the "phlogiston" theory in chemistry, not contested until the time of Lavoisier. Exerted a strong influence on the vitalists of the school of Montpellier.

His basic and influential theory of diseases was that of "animism" and it arose as a reaction to iatrophysics and iatrochemistry which predominated at the time. According to Stahl, the chemical and physical reactions of the body are kept going only by means of the soul (anima) and disease was a fight between the anima and harmful influences. This view dealt a blow at the old Somaticism which had governed psychiatric thinking from Hippocrates to Stahl. Even where somaticism survived, it was in a richer, more complex form. Stahl himself wrote little in any detail about insanity. His basic division of mental illnesses however into "sympathetic" (that is, due to disease of organs) and "pathetic" (that is, functional with no organic basis) was widely accepted and was crucial for the whole subsequent development of psychiatry. It is probably also due to Stahl that in the eighteenth century so many men, such as Ch. G. Ludwig (1758), Zueckert (1764), Harper (1789), Fischer (1790), and Langermann (1797) suddenly came forward with theories about the psychological causation of mental disease. It is also no coincidence that most of them were German since it was in Germany that philosophical idealism triumphed in the eighteenth century. The fact that many of these so-called psychological causes later proved false and turned out to be symptoms rather than causes of mental illness is here of only secondary importance.

Not only was somaticism accompanied by psychologism in the eighteenth century, it was itself completely changed. Until then somaticists had largely been humoralists, followers of Hippocrates and Galen. But now the basic theories about disease became increasingly more "solidistic" and these views were, of course, shared by psychiatrists. The trends towards solidism and localism were strengthened enormously by the work of the pathological anatomists, above all by that of Morgagni (1761) who performed autopsies on numerous mentally ill patients. This new solidism of the eighteenth century was based especially on the study of the nervous system, about which many important physiological discoveries were now being made. Here, as so often in the history of medicine, new discoveries led to the over-emphasis of isolated phenomena and to the development of generalizations derived from these which were not justified by the facts. The experimental discoveries of Albrecht von Haller (1752) on the sensitivity of the nervous system and on the irritability of muscles (contractibility) were at once converted by Cullen of Edinburgh (1769) into a general explanation of disease as due to nervous disorders. Cullen coined the term "neurosis"[2] and recommended the use of the straight-jacket invented by McBride. Robert Whytt's first experiments (1751) with reflexes, which he still called "sympathy" and the experiments by Galvani and Volta (both 1792) with "animal" electricity had similar results. This belated discovery of the nervous system was responsible for the fact that the illnesses which we now call neuroses and which had until then been thought of as due to "vapors" or to "decay of the humors," were now attributed to the nervous system. Only since the eighteenth century has it ben possible to suffer from "nerves."

The eighteenth century also saw the beginning of studies on cerebral localization (Pourfour du Petit, Lorry, Gall, Swedenborg[3]), which were to be of such crucial importance for psychiatry. A product of the late eighteenth century was the medical philosopher, Pierre Cabanis (1757-1808)[4], a theorist who combined the psychological and somatic viewpoints. Although his writings seem full of platitudes to us today, he exerted an enormous influence on medicine, psychiatry, education, politics and even literature which lasted for several decades. Cabanis belonged to the school of ideologists and became a friend and protector of Pinel. He was one of the later philosophers of enlightenment and a sensualist. In his famous *"Traité du Physique et du Moral de l'Homme"* (1799), he was primarily concerned to explain "moral," that is psychological phenomena on a physiological basis. He also demonstrated however that moral impressions can have physiological and pathological results. Thus at last a rational explanation was provided for the

[2] For the historical development of the concept of neurosis see J. M. Lopez Pinero's excellent book: *Origines historicas del concepte de neuroses*, Valencia, 1963.

[3] Cited in Akert, K. and Hammond, M. P., *Medical History*, 6: 255-266, 1962.

[4] Pierre Jean Georges Cabanis, born 1757. At first a writer, 1783 qualified as doctor of medicine in Paris. A friend of Turgot, Madame Helvetius, Holbach, Franklin, Jefferson, Condillac, Diderot, d'Alembert, Condorcet. Together with Destutt de Tracy, leader of the "ideologues" (sensualist philosophers). Concerned with educational reform. Physician of Mirabeau. 1794, professor of Hygiene at the new École de Santé. 1796, member of the Institute. 1797, professor of clinical medicine. 1798, member of the Council of 500; aided Napoleon in his coup d'état. Member of the Senate and administrator of Parisian hospitals. Later, together with his friends, bereft of his influence by Napoleon. Died 1808.

psychological production of disease in which the so-called "passions" were held in those days to play a specially important role. For the first time also a theoretical explanation was provided for "moral" treatment, that is for psychotherapy. Psychotherapy had after all been theoretically impossible both on the basis of the older somaticism and on the basis of the old beliefs about the soul. From the middle of the eighteenth century we find an increasing number of books appearing which recommend psychotherapy not only for mental illnesses but also for ordinary physical complaints. We mention here only the works of Bolten (1751), Scheidemantel (1787), Tissot (1782), Falconer (1789), Haslam (1798), and Reil (1803). This was a progressive move despite the fact that one can hardly support the methods of healing by means of fear which were advocated by many writers. It was not until Pinel that fear was banished from the arsenal of psychotherapy. Apart from books by learned doctors, there was a second source of psychotherapy in psychiatry. Because of the current state of affairs treatment of the insane was largely in the hands of the chief warders of institutions and not in those of the physicians. Among these chief warders were many intelligent and humane individuals who discovered, often before the doctors did, that psychotherapy was more effective than the usual methods of purgation and blood-letting.

The eighteenth century in psychiatry is unfortunately not only the century of the development of psychotherapy but also the century of the active development of physical treatment methods which might be regarded as a sort of shock therapy. The old "treatment" by ducking was supplemented by the so-called Darwin chair (invented by Charles Darwin's grandfather, the physician Erasmus Darwin, 1731-1802). In this chair the insane were rotated until blood oozed from their mouths, ears and noses, and for years most successful cures were reported as a result of its use. Castration and starvation cures were also employed. Old drugs, such as datura and camphor, were introduced once more and the newly discovered drug, digitalis, was used in large quantities to treat cases of insanity as well as all other types of disease. Magnetic cures, used in the seventeenth century, continued to be popular and electricity was introduced as a treatment method.

The large number of text books which appeared during this period testify to the magnitude of the psychiatric movement in the eighteenth century. We would mention only the works of Battie

(1758, he made an early attempt to teach psychiatry in London) ;
of Arnold (1782, he worked on a new classification) ; Perfect (1787,
he was one of the few writers who reported case histories and who
tried out treatment with electricity and calomel) ; Pargeter (1792) ;
Harper (1789) ; Faulkner (1790) ; Haslam (1798, he was apothecary
to the famous and notorious Bedlam Hospital in London until his
dismissal on account of the appalling conditions there in 1816) ;
and of Crichton (1798). Great Britain, which was at that time in
the forefront of clinical medicine, also produced most of the psychiatric work. But we must also mention the works of French
writers, particularly Lorry (1762), Le Camus (1769) and Dufour
(1770). Colombier and Doublet (1785) as well as Daquin (1791)
attempted even before Pinel to effect reforms in the treatment of
mental diseases. Among the writings in the German language we
must refer to those of Auenbrugger, the inventor of percussion
(Vienna, 1776). Auenbrugger reported interesting cases of insanity
which he attributed to shrinkage of the penis, as in the case of
"Koro" among the Chinese in Java.[5] Furthermore mention should
be made of the books of Greding (1757, with many autopsy reports), Zimmerman (1784), Klockhof (1772), Fischer (1790),
Langermann (1797) and Reil (1803) who incidentally coined the
term psychiatry.[6] The first American book on mental diseases,
written by the famous Benjamin Rush[7] (*Medical Inquiry and Observations upon the Diseases of the Mind,* Philadelphia, 1812) also
belongs to eighteenth century currents of thought. Pinel's *"Traité
medico-philosophique sur l'Aliénation Mentale,"* which first ap-

5 Ducret, Jos., *Auenbrugger als Psychiater,* Zürich, 1955.

6 Johann Christian Reil, born 1759 at Rhaude in Ostfriesland. Graduated in
Halle, 1782. After 1787, professor there. 1810, professor of Medicine at the newly
founded University of Berlin. 1813, died of battle typhus. Vitalist, later "Natur-
philosoph," neuro-anatomist. Campaigned unsuccessfully for the foundation of
psychiatric institutes in Berlin and Halle.

7 Benjamin Rush, born near Philadelphia in 1745. Studied and qualified in
1768 in Edinburgh after the six-year apprenticeship which was at that time
customary in America. 1769, professor of Chemistry at the newly founded first
North American School of Medicine in Philadelphia and, after 1789, professor
of Medicine. Very influential teacher. One of the signatories of the Declaration
of Independence. Chief physician of Washington's army 1778, and, after 1799,
director of the Mint. Social reformer who campaigned against the death penalty,
slavery, alcoholism, maltreatment of the insane, inflation, etc. Famous in medicine, particularly as opponent of the theory of contagiousness of yellow fever
and as an unremitting advocate of blood-letting and purgation. Died 1813.

peared in 1801, represents both the pinnacle of eighteenth century psychiatry and, at the same time, the beginning of a new epoch.

A brief summary of Dr. William Battie's (1704-1776) *Treatise on Madness* which appeared in London in 1758, and which is typical of the period, will indicate the general tenor of eighteenth century psychiatric writings.

Characteristically Battie begins with a chapter called "Definition of Madness" and throughout his book this experienced clinician presents us with not a single case history. He sees madness as false imagination. A number of chapters are devoted to the site of natural emotions, their apparent and actual causes, and their life preserving functions. Anxiety states are frequent precursors of mental illness; dementia is a common end state. Battie takes up his central theme only in chapter 7! For him there are two main groups of insanity: primary insanity, due solely to defects of nervous tissue, and secondary (consequential) insanity, due to somatic causes, such as head injury, excessive exposure to the sun, spasms, fever, poisons, passions, gluttony, laziness etc. The author then deals with the differential diagnosis, prognosis and treatment of both forms of illness. He mentions innumerable obnoxious and dangerous treatment methods but finally exhorts his reader to use all these sparingly and declares himself ever hopeful that spontaneous recovery will occur.

The writings of eighteenth century psychiatrists must be admired and welcomed for the good intentions and progressive views they express. Yet it is difficult to ignore the fact that, in line with the trends of the period, they contain far too many speculations, theories and classifications and deal much too cursorily with descriptions and studies of actual case histories. All too often eighteenth century writers tried to force mental illnesses into one of the "systems" so dear to their hearts and, again in line with the general attitudes of the day, they were far too preoccupied with disturbances of intellect and reason. Radical changes in these trends were to be brought about by Pinel and his school.

CHAPTER VI

PINEL, ESQUIROL AND THE FRENCH SCHOOL

PHILIPPE Pinel, a doctor's son, was born in 1745 in a small village in the South of France. At first destined to take up theology, he changed over to mathematics and later to medicine which he studied in Toulouse and Montpellier. In 1778 he moved to Paris. His development was slow and even then he did not commit himself entirely to the practice of medicine. His main energies went into scientific studies; he earned his living as a tutor and also undertook translations and editorial work. He became the friend of Cabanis and Thouret, and a member of the salon of ideologists who met at the house of Madame Helvetius. As far as we know, his interest in psychiatry began only in the mid-eighties, when he was forty years old. The revolution, which brought temporary power to many of his friends, also raised the shy and unpretentious Pinel to positions of prominence: In 1793 he was put in charge of the Bicêtre Asylum and in 1795 of the Salpêtrière, where he accomplished his famous work of liberation. Finally, in 1794, he was made Professor of Hygiene and, later, of Internal Medicine in the newly-founded School of Medicine. Among his contemporaries he was known and admired as a physician rather than a psychiatrist. His *Nosography,* which appeared in 1798, became the bible of the Paris school for twenty years. For us the predominant interest lies of course in his *"Traité médico-philosophique sur l'Aliénation Mentale"* (at first called *"Traité de la Manie"*) which was first published in 1801. During the "purge" of liberalism, which took place in the medical school in 1822, Pinel was forced to retire and he died in 1826.

His *Traité,* a basic text of modern psychiatry, begins with a critical review of the work of his predecessors. Characteristically Pinel at once stresses the achievements of his warders in reforming the treatment of the insane, mentioning in particular his collaborator, Pussin, whom in many ways he regarded as his teacher. He also highlights the contributions of his favorite pupil, Esquirol. Equally characteristic is his own description of his work as philanthropic. The complaint that he failed to mention Daquin as his teacher is misplaced since this well-meaning but gullible provincial in fact had nothing to teach him.[1] Pinel announces that he does not intend to discuss the various hypotheses about the human understanding, its seat and its nature. His task as a natural scientist is, he says, to observe facts and to bring some order into the chaos of the current treatment methods by means of critical and objective (statistical) investigations.

He turns first to the problem of the causation of mental illnesses. He points out that the patient's emotional life is often disturbed before the onset of the actual attack and he emphasises the importance of psychological factors in the development of insanity. Heredity is for him the first cause. The second is harmful factors in the social environment, such as for example educational factors. A faulty education can, he says, lead to a true pseudo-dementia. On the other hand, treatment of the insane is, according to him, only a form of education. The third cause is an irregular way of life. The fourth is what he calls spasmodic passions (rage, fright) and the fifth, enervating or oppressive passions (grief, hate, fear, remorse). He also mentions the dangers of a change-over from an active to an inactive mode of life (the psychological difficulties of retired people were already well known in the eighteenth century) as well as the conflicts between instincts and religious dogma. A sixth cause he sees in the gay passions and a seventh in the melancholic constitution. Physical factors are mentioned only as the eighth cause and among these he includes alcoholism, amenorrhoea, non-bleeding haemorrhoids, fever, the puerperium and head injury.

He next presents a general symptomatology of mental diseases. In mania he describes an increase of body temperature, of physical strength, appetite and sexual desire. He frankly discusses the occurrence of masturbation and homosexuality in asylums. Perception of external objects may be disturbed. Thinking may be completely confused but in cases of so-called "folie raisonnante" thinking remains clear although the patients are insane. Pinel and Esquirol's preoccupation with these phenomena is proof of their final emancipation from the theory of possession, which was then still widely

---

[1] S. Nyffeler, J. R., *Jos. Daquin*, Zürich, 1961.

STRAIT-JACKET
(from Esquirol's book)

ESQUIROL

held and according to which the mentally ill patient could only be viewed as completely insane. According to Pinel the thoughts of melancholics are concentrated on a single object. Memory and association of ideas may be disturbed. Pinel here describes a case of aphasia with agraphia and alexia. Disturbances of judgment are particularly striking in folie raisonnante. Dements and idiots can simulate normal powers of judgment because of their imitative faculties. Mental illness affects mainly the emotions. Raving is far more characteristic of mania than false ideas or false judgments. The emotional life undergoes a complete change and apathetic stupor may supervene. The imgaination may be disturbed as in hypochondriasis where patients may believe that they have no heart or that their limbs are made of glass or that they have been changed into wolves. The crucial factor is an alteration of character and a return to the premorbid character is a precursor of recovery.

Pinel then presents his classification of mental diseases. He mocks Cullen and Erasmus Darwin who looked upon even simple vices as mental illnesses: "Ce serait convertir en petites maisons (private mental hospitals) nos cités les plus florissantes." His classification on the whole conforms to the classical models. He recognizes only four forms of mental illness: mania, melancholia, dementia and idiocy. There is no parallel in any of our present diseases for his concept of mania or general delirium which covers essentially all types of agitated states. These, according to Pinel, have their site in the region of the stomach. Plato's old idea was now brought up to date by Cabanis and Pinel who found the site of mania in the nervous ganglia of the abdominal cavity. In mania, according to Pinel, one sees bizarre, abnormally jolly and also sad behavior. The course of mania, like that of any acute illness, is self limited and recovery is often possible since it is a "purely nervous" disorder not accompanied by organic changes. Mania can also consist of disturbances of the emotional life alone without delirium.

Pinel suggests "exclusive delirium" as an alternative name for melancholia. He rejects too wide an extension of this concept and reserves the term "melancholia" for cases in which the mind is concentrated on a single idea which may be either sad or grandiose. Melancholics may be mute for years. Melancholia may also degenerate into mania. It often leads to suicide and to refusal of food and is characterized by the presence of obsessional ideas and illusions.

Dementia or absence of thinking is mainly due to exhaustion following sexual excesses. Thinking becomes totally incoherent and this distinguishes dementia from mania. In the latter ideas are false but coherent, whereas in the former they are completely isolated from one another.

Idiocy is characterized by the absence of all intellectual faculties. It is very common, is often associated with abnormalities of the skull, and is generally treated far too energetically. The discussion of idiocy leads Pinel on to the topics of cretinism and the legal problems in psychiatry.

If we attempt to group the disease pictures recognized today according to the old classification, we find that "mania" includes cases of schizophrenia as well as hypomania; "melancholia" includes genuine depressions and also depressed schizophrenics and cases of paranoia, neurosis and general paresis. "Dementia" includes cases of general paresis, paranoia, schizophrenia and neurosis. The old categories are in fact not founded on real disease pictures but on symptomatic states.

Of the greatest importance for Pinel are the principles underlying the organization and administration of mental hospitals. In his hands the hospital becomes the main therapeutic tool. He calls for an attitude that is vigorous but also liberal and confidence inspiring. Institutions must above all be large enough to allow different types of patients to be segregated from each other. He describes the Salpêtrière, with its separate departments for idiots and thieves, for incurable agitated patients, for curable agitated patients, for quiet patients (dements), for senile dements and for convalescents (with workshops). In addition there is a hospital section for mentally ill patients who also suffer from other diseases.

He naturally rejects completely the use of chains as a method of correction, having himself abolished them in the Bicêtre and the Salpêtrière. He does resort to the use of the strait-jacket but warns against using this for too long a period. Both the strait-jacket and the douche may, according to him, be ordered only by the physician. Continuity, the maintenance of a constant routine, and the study of the patient's personality are essential. He regards the division of administrative powers between the medical and administrative heads as one of the major difficulties of hospital organization, one that has led to an almost grotesque state of affairs in most institutions. Recovered patients, he says, often make good nurses. Food must be distributed with strict fairness. In times of famine the death rate in mental hospitals rises steeply. Physical exercise or mechanical work should, as in Saragossa and Amsterdam, form the basic program of every mental hospital. Work is of particular importance for idiots. That is why members of the nobility, who reject such activities, are especially difficult to cure. Psychotherapeutic measures must be based on the authority and expert knowledge of the physician who is sometimes forced to use guile. Religious activities should be carefully restricted because they sometimes provoke dangerous states of ecstasy. Both Pinel and Esquirol were deeply convinced of the absolute necessity for an early separation of the patient from his family since the family cannot look after him properly and only produces unnecessary strain. Connections with the outside world in general should be strictly limited. Experience both in France and in England has shown that too early a resumption of contact with the outside world can lead to a dangerous relapse. Some seditious and incorrigible thieves should be nursed apart from the rest of the patients.

The treatment of melancholics demands great skill. Among the case histories presented to illustrate this one finds incidentally cases which we would today classify as paranoia or obsessional neurosis. In cases of food refusal Pinel introduced tube feeding with great success. He warns against suicide as an ever-present danger and remarks that it is usually necessary to supervise the hospital staff as carefully as the patients.

Pinel then reviews the old and the more recent methods used for the treatment of the insane. Beating, used liberally since the time of Celsus, he rejects as an ineffective measure in treatment and, incidentally, also in education. Neither does he think much of phlebotomy. Sudden ducking, still recommended by Boerhaave, he describes as "a medical delirium, more serious than the delirium of patients." On the other hand he is a firm believer in the efficacy of baths and also uses douches in moderation. Here he reports some interesting experiments with the douche which Esquirol performed on himself. Both ducking and ice-cold douches were still used in the twentieth century by the secret police of certain countries to elicit confessions from their victims.

It is important to isolate excited patients in the early stages of mania. One must avoid confusing mania with febrile delirium. Fetters should be applied only to the most agitated patients and then not for long. Patients must be well fed and must have much outdoor exercise. Baths and mild laxatives are helpful. One should always use drugs very sparingly. Melancholia, according to Pinel, is even more difficult to treat than mania which tends to have a natural course and thus, according to Hippocratic theory, a tendency to spontaneous remission. He stresses the benefits of moral treatment and of work therapy. Possession and exorcism he regards as nonsense. Pinel prefers more harmless purgatives to the traditional hellebore. He also uses sedatives such as camphor and opium. Mania can sometimes end during a crisis, such as results for example from a parotid abscess or a general febrile illness. It is extremely difficult to decide when a case is cured and the greatest care is indicated at the time of discharge of convalescent patients.

Pinel then presents the results of his statistical investigations which he considers to be of great importance. Mania he finds primarily between puberty and the age of 45; in women it may begin even earlier. Melancholia is mainly found between the ages of 20 and 40. Of particular importance in melancholia are moral, that is psychological, causes such as fright, disappointment in love, loss of property, domestic difficulties and exaggerated piety. Among the physical causes the most obvious ones are constitutional factors, amenorrhoea and the puerperium. He obtains 51% of cures in cases of mania, 62% in melancholia, 19% in dementia and none at all in cases of idiocy. The average length of treatment is 5½ months in cases of mania, 6½ months in cases of melancholia. He has had 71 relapses among 444 patients. Since most of his incurables received unfavorable treatment elsewhere before coming to him his results would probably have been even better had they come to him direct. In this connection he makes the interesting observation that if insanity is complicated by paralysis, recovery never occurs.

In incurable cases he thinks that one would probably find organic damage, although the results of morbid anatomical investigations have so far been contradictory. It has often been claimed that abnormalities are found in the abdomen. Skull measurements yield significant results only in cases of idiocy. Moral causes are especially important at certain periods of life or in certain occupations (monks, artists). Physicians and mathematicians rarely become insane. Failure to recover may be due to the onset of other diseases, and here hysteria, epilepsy and hypochondriasis are particularly dangerous. The impossibility of organizing work therapy in certain institutions has very unfortunate reprecussions. The most difficult patients to treat are the malicious, the wealthy and those accustomed to wield power. Treatment is facilitated to the extent that it can be based on moral values. But progress in ethics[2] has not been as rapid during the eighteenth century as progress in the natural sciences. Educational reform in this direction is most urgent. He hopes that his book will be a contribution to this field in that it demonstrates the tragic results of the neglect of moral values.

In summary, we can say that the most characteristic features of Pinel's psychiatric attitude which, although rooted in the eighteenth century, marks the beginning of a new epoch, are the following: his indifference to theories and classifications; his strong emphasis on the observation of clinical phenomena and on statistics; his "Hippocratism," that is, his expectant attitude as an observer; his ethics; his preference for psychogenic aetiological explanations; his fascination by "folie raisonnante," that is, mania without intellectual disturbances; and his "philanthropie" as manifested by his activities as a reformer and humanitarian, his generosity and benevolence and his belief in the possibility of curing mental illness. Pinel's strength lay without doubt in his gifts as a helper and therapist. He saw himself primarily as a clinician and from the point of view of formal dogmatism he was an "eclectic." So were most of the significant psychiatrists after him and this attitude still seems, perhaps because of the youthfulness of psychiatry, to be the most fruitful one; just as it was in the case of internal medicine in a similarly early phase at the time of Boerhaave.

As a physician Pinel had many eminent pupils (Bichat, Broussais, Landré-Beauvais, Schwilguè, etc.). As a psychiatrist he had only two: Guillaume Ferrus (1784-1861), who earned renown in the field of work therapy and mental hospital reform, and Esquirol.[3] Jean-Etienne-Dominique Esquirol (1772-1840) came from the same district of France as did Pinel and, like him, he was the son of a doctor, destined to take up theology. He too studied at Toulouse and Montpellier and he too entered psychiatry relatively late in life. In 1799 he came to Paris and joined Pinel. In 1811 he became

2 Pinel's attitude applied not only to his practice of psychiatry but of medicine. It was shared by almost all members of the illustrious Paris school (1800-1850) of which Pinel was the first head. See Ackerknecht, E. H., *Medicine in the Paris Hospital 1794-1848*, Baltimore, 1966.

3 Moreover, his Geneva pupil, Matthey, described kleptomania. See Müllener, R. E., *Entstehung des Kleptomaniebegriffes*, Sudhoffs Archiv. 48: 216-239, 1964.

his colleague on the staff of the Salpêtrière. One can describe Esquirol's basic attitudes in exactly the same terms as those we have just used for Pinel. In spite of this, however, the unique and surprising fact remains that Esquirol was by no means merely a paler edition of his teacher; on the contrary, he was able to achieve even more in the same fields than his master, who was always ready to acknowledge this without a trace of envy. In addition, Esquirol was a gifted teacher. He held the first series of lectures in psychiatry in 1817. He trained many outstanding French and foreign students[4] and was responsible for the pre-eminence of the French School of Psychiatry in the first half of the nineteenth century. His achievements in the field of public health[5] were also quite remarkable. In contrast to Laennec he was popular among his liberal students and colleagues despite his royalist views. He had a great love for his profession and for his patients and, like many of his predecessors and many of his successors, he still lived together with his patients. He was however greatly hurt by the fact that these, when cured, often behaved in public as if they did not know him. Louis Leuret, Moreau, Calmeil, Baillarger, and his nephew, Mitivié, gathered around his deathbed, and his last words were: "Live in peace."

Esquirol was a better statistician than Pinel and his clinical observations and descriptions were clearer, more detailed and more accurate. Progressive paresis as well as circular insanity and Jacksonian epilepsy can be recognized among his descriptions. He also was an "eclectic" and his remark: "Il ne faut jamais être absolu dans la pratique" is epigrammatic. Moreover, he was the more imaginative psychotherapist. He was extraordinarily unbiased and would try out anything that promised some sort of success even if he distrusted it. This applied to mesmerism, Gall's phrenology, treatment with music and morbid anatomy. He was however not at all enthusiastic about the famous and, at that time, so controversial colony for the insane at Gheel in Belgium which had sprung up in the former place of pilgrimage. He was free from all prejudices, such as for example the still accepted climatism of Hippocrates or the enlightened anti-clericalism of Pinel. Nor did he

---

[4] Lists of the French pupils of Esquirol in *Pariset, E., Éloges*, Vol. 2, pp. 476, 482.

[5] See Ackerknecht, E. H., *Hygiene in France 1815-1848, Bull. Hist. Med.* 22: 117-155, 1948.

succumb to new myths such as, for instance, that of the "worthy" poor. He freed himself from Pinel's theory of the gastro-intestinal localization of mania and adopted Gall's theory of cerebral localization. The interpretation of mental illnesses in terms of diseases of the brain is without doubt attributable mainly to F. J. Gall who, despite his "phrenology," made numerous and valuable contributions to the anatomy, physiology and pathology of the brain.[6] Esquirol had a deeper understanding of the "moral" causes of insanity and he recognized that some of the so-called causes, e.g. abuse of alcohol and masturbation, were often merely early symptoms. He saw much more clearly the roles that social upheavals and the isolation of modern man play in the genesis of mental illness. His account is here reminiscent of Stendhal. It is not a coincidence that one of the French terms for mental disease is "aliénation," that is estrangement. In the course of such diseases human relationships are disrupted and may even be changed into their opposites. On the other hand he pointed out how much the mental patient and the normal person have in common, particularly when the latter's attention wanders. The mental patient loses the capacity for concentration. Esquirol differentiated between hallucinations and illusions. His work on the subject of hallucinations was continued by Alexandre Brièrre de Boismont (1798-1881) who did much work with criminals. Esquirol developed Pinel's ideas about "folie raisonnante" in his teaching about the monomanias or partial insanities, which was however rejected by many of his pupils, e.g. J. P. Falret, Trélat, Foville. Another name he gave to melancholia was lypemania and he followed Pinel in thinking that the content of delirium in these cases consists only of a single object.

The still unsettled question of whether mental diseases are increasing in our society Esquirol discussed at length, using statistical evidence. He believed that any increase was more apparent than real. The answer to this question would of course also settle the issue of whether civilization produces more mental illness than other cultures. In the light of this discussion it becomes at once apparent why medical men of different nationalities have from time to time (in England in the eighteenth, in America in the

6 See Ackerknecht, E. H., and Vallois, H. V., *François Joseph Gall et sa collection,* Paris, 1955. Gall strongly influenced many contemporary psychiatrists, among them Georget, F. Voisin, John Conolly, R. Willis, Isaac Ray, Amariah Brigham, Miraglia.

nineteenth century) pointed almost with pride to their wealth of neurotics. If civilization produces mental diseases, then the country with the largest number of patients must be the most civilized.

Esquirol the reformer was no less successful than Esquirol the research worker. The French legal code of 1838 relating to mental health administration was designated by him and is the first comprehensive legislation in this field (a partial law had existed in England since 1828). It served as a model for similar legislation in Switzerland (1838), England (1842), and Norway (1848). His private sanatorium in Ivry and his institution at Charenton, which were built according to his own plans and which he administered from 1826, were model institutions. Charenton (at present under the direction of Professor Baruk who lovingly guards Esquirol's beautiful library) is to this day a remarkable place. The asylums in Saint-Yon, Le Mans, Montpellier and Marseilles were also built according to his plans. In this connection attention should be drawn to the fact that special institutions were at last being created for the care of feeble-minded and idiots. J. E. Belhomme (1824) was the first to found such an institution and he was followed by Ferrus (1828); Felix Voisin (1834); and Eduard Seguin (1839), whose work in America after 1848 developed in a most fruitful way. A special role was played between 1820 and 1893 by the private institution in Paris run by Dr. Esprit Blanche and his son Emile. Here many mentally ill "gens du monde" and especially artists from Nerval to Maupassant found a place of asylum.[7]

Esquirol's influence continued to be felt until the eighties of the last century because of his pupils: J. J. Moreau de Tours (1804-1884), about whom more will be said in connection with the degeneration theory, and J. Baillarger (1809-1890) who in 1850 described, among other things, the pupillary changes in general paresis. Baillarger and Moreau together with Cérise and Brierre were also responsible for establishing the important *"Annales médico-psychologiques"* in 1843.

Of the other pupils of Esquirol only the most important can be mentioned. Etienne Jean Georget (1795-1828) his favorite student, the friend of the painter Guéricault, died young. His main work dealt with legal psychiatry and the cerebral localization of all men-

---

[7] Le Breton, J., *La Maison de Santé du Docteur Blanche,* Paris Th. 1937.

tal diseases including hysteria. The preface to his *"Physiologie du système nerveux"* sounds like a preliminary study to Claude Bernard's *"Introduction à la Médecine Expérimentale."* François Leuret (1797-1851) became the advocate of a generally rather foolish type of "moral" treatment and thus took a step backwards to the time before Pinel. His clear-sighted psychological observations however were still quoted by Freud and Janet. Jean-Pierre Falret (1794-1870), who must not be confused with his son Jules (1824-1902), began his work with studies on suicide, a subject which has always held a particular fascination for French sociologists and psychiatrists. He began as a somaticist but his attitudes became more and more those of a psychologist. He was the first to describe circular insanity (1853). He also introduced an important social innovation: insurance for discharged patients (1843). Together with his friend Felix Voisin (1794-1872), not to be confused with the latter's nephew Auguste Voisin (1829-1998), he founded the famous private hospital in Vanves. Voisin, who was much influenced by Gall, devoted himself above all to the study and training of the feeble-minded. Achille Foville (1799-1878) is renowned mainly for his neuro-anatomical studies. Louis Florentin Calmeil (1798-1895), another pupil of Esquirol, was one of the first to recognize dementia paralytica as a separate disease (1826) and is the author of a classical history of mass psychoses. It was not however a member of Esquirol's school who could claim the discovery of progressive paralysis as a separate disease picture, but Antoine Laurent Bayle (1799-1858) whom Esquirol's school had caused to leave psychiatry altogether. Bayle was a nephew of Gaspard Laurent Bayle, a disciple of Laennec's and a pupil of A. Royer-Collard. He had already described the clinical and neuro-pathological stages of progressive paralysis in his thesis of 1822.[8] His discovery was of immense importance. Not only was the then most prevalent mental disease identified, but it was shown to have an organic basis and, for the first time, the natural history of a psychiatric disease entirely replaced descriptions of purely symptomatic states.

In the first half of the century some of the followers of Pinel and Esquirol were responsible for considerable developments in Forensic Psychiatry and special mention must here be made of Ch. H. Marc

[8] Müller, Stefan, *Antoine Laurent Bayle*, Zürich, 1965.

(1771-1850) .[9] During this period psychiatric teaching everywhere was modelled on Esquirol's methods and official chairs of psychiatry were not created until the eighteen-seventies.[10]

Although, as Henri Ey has shown,[11] differences between the psychological and the somatic orientations are noticeable in France too, they never developed into a fundamental dichotomy there as they did in Germany at that time. Among those with a psychological orientation were Pinel, Fodéré, Esquirol, Lélut, Falret, Baillarger and especially the Belgian, Guislain. Those who thought primarily along somatic lines included Ferrus, Calmeil, Prost, Georget, Bottex, Voisin, Foville and Moreau. The strength of the somatic orientation can be traced as much to the then very powerful influences of Gall and Broussais[12] as to the contemporaneous successes in the field of morbid anatomy of the nervous system achieved by Rostan, Lallemand, Bouillaud, Andral, Rochoux, Parent-Duchatelet and Martinet and, above all, by Bayle and Calmeil. The materialistic tradition in French philosophy also played its part. Finally the somatic orientation gained the upper hand even in France and assumed the peculiar form of the degeneration theory.

In this same period Great Britain produced only one psychiatrist of note. This was the Quaker, James Cowles Prichard (1785-1848), also known as an anthropologist. He struggled with the same problem of "monomania" as did Pinel and Esquirol and created the category of "moral insanity." The great English contribution to international psychiatry of that period was the introduction of the system of "no restraint" which also did without the strait-jacket. Robert Gardner Hill laid down the principles of "no restraint" at Lincoln in 1829 and Charlesworth and John Conolly[13] fought for

---

[9] For details see Bass, G., *Die Gerichtsmedizin als Spezialfach in Paris 1800-1850,* Zürich, 1964.

[10] See Ackerknecht, E. H., *Zur Geschichte der Lehr—und Forschungsstätten für Psychiatrie in Europa,* in Kolle, K., *Grosse Nervenärzte,* Vol. 2, pp. 223-230, Stuttgart, 1958.

[11] Ey. H., *Études Psychiatriques,* Vol. 1, p. 34, Paris, 1948.

[12] Ackerknecht, E. H., *Broussais. Bull. Hist. Med.* 27: 320-343, 1953.

[13] John Conolly, born 1794 at Market Rasen, Lincolnshire. At first a soldier. Spent some time with his brother, William, a practitioner in Tours, France. Did not begin medical studies until 1817 in Edinburgh. 1821-27, country doctor. 1828, Professor of Practical Medicine at University College, London. 1830-38, Warwick. After 1839, physician to Hanwell, a large mental hospital near London. Prolific writer and one of the founders of the British Medical Association. Died 1866.

them at Hanwell in 1839. Conolly also began once more to teach psychiatry and his son-in-law, the astute Henry Maudsley (1835-1918), was the most widely known English psychiatrist of his generation.

CHAPTER VII

THE THEORY OF DEGENERATION

ABOUT the middle of the nineteenth century the somaticists went through a period of disillusionment. Except in the senile psychoses and in general paralysis the results obtained from anatomical studies of the brain had not come up to expectation. In contrast to the diseases of heart, lungs, intestines, etc., no objective foundation had been found for the symptoms of mental disease. A new idea was then advanced—the degeneration hypothesis[1]—which seemed to solve the problem of "somaticism": it held out hopes of establishing unequivocal physical signs of mental illness, more tangible than the variable changes hitherto demonstrated in the brain, and hopes too of synthesising all known facts and finally arriving at an aetiological rather than a symptomatic classification of mental disorders. This idea came to the fore almost at the same time as the Darwinian theory and because it could so readily be brought into line with Darwinism, it gained enormous popularity among psychiatrists as well as in all classes of the general population. However attractive in its own right, the degeneration hypothesis would never have acquired the significance it did if it had not coincided with the Darwinian theory, then sweeping all before it. From the therapeutic standpoint degeneration was a pessimistic idea, but the philosophy of the period was predominantly pessimistic; so also was the climate of thought among psychiatrists, working as they did almost entirely in mental hospitals with what seemed to be mostly hopeless cases.

This important concept too originated in France. It developed from ideas about heredity and mental illness which were already old

---

[1] In the preparation of this chapter I have drawn largely from the excellent book by Georges Genil-Perrin: *"Histoire des Origines et de l'évolution de l'idée de dégénérescence en médecine mentale."* Paris, 1913. See also Burgener, P., *"Die Einflüsse des zeitgenössischen Denkens in Morels Begriff der 'Dégénérescence,'"* Zürich, 1964.

BEDLAM as seen by HOGARTH

EMIL KRAEPELIN

and which had been held by Perfect, Burrows, Pinel, Esquirol, Marc, Falret père and Baillarger. Rush, Kirkbride and Woodward had, it is true, greatly restricted the part played by heredity, reflecting no doubt the lack of sympathy which Anglo-Saxons in general have always shown towards "pessimistic" studies such as those on heredity or constitution. Prosper Lucas's work: *"Traité philosophique et physiologique de l'hérédité naturelle"* (Paris, 1847) had given great impetus to genetic research in psychiatry. The theory of degeneration had already been formulated by J. Moreau de Tours (1804-1884) who since 1850 had been shifting the emphasis in aetiology towards a multiform hereditary predisposition which could, for example, account also for scrofula and rickets and which could be recognized by so-called stigmata. His experimental work on hashish was of more value and led him to describe insanity as a "rêve éveillé."

The real creator of the degeneration theory was Benedict Augustin Morel (1809-1873) who was born in Vienna of French parents. Morel and his friends Claude Bernard, Lasègue and Davaine, were penniless medical students who had to earn their living by giving private lessons. Bernard had introduced Morel to Jean Pierre Falret whose pupil he became. In addition to these influences Morel was greatly impressed by the anthropological studies of Gall, Blainville, Flourens and Serres. With Buchez and Cérise he belonged to a small group of medical men who combined political radicalism with most devout Catholicism and were the pioneers of a social orientation in medicine.

His theory of degeneration reflects all these influences. The hypothesis is at once psychiatric and socio-anthropological. To him degeneration is as much a religious as a scientific concept and in this he differs as much from the older naturalists, Buffon and Blumenbach, who used the term to mean variation, as from the newer biologists like Heusinger, to whom it meant atavism. To Morel, as a pious Christian, such concepts were foreign. He defines degeneration as follows: "Les dégénérations sont des déviations maladives du type normal de l'humanité héréditairement transmissibles et évoluant progressivement vers la déchéance." (Degenerations are deviations from the normal human type which are transmissible by heredity and which deteriorate progressively towards extinction.) Morel worked on this problem from 1839 onwards, and gave it its final form in the *"Traité des Dégénérescences*

Physiques, Intéllectuelles et Morales de l'Espèce Humaine" which appeared in 1857. According to him, degeneration could be caused by: (1) intoxication (malaria, alcohol, opium, soil conducive to cretinism, epidemics, food poisoning) ; (2) the social milieu; (3) pathological temperament; (4) moral sickness; (5) inborn or acquired damage; (6) heredity. The combined effect of physical and moral injuries was particularly dangerous ("law of two-fold fertilization"). Degeneration was also subject to the "law of progressivity." The first generation of a degenerate family might be merely nervous, the second would tend to be neurotic, the third psychotic, while the fourth consisted of idiots and died out. Because such diseases and diseased families were becoming more frequent, modern society was inevitably approaching extinction. By means of a very hazy concept of "hereditary predisposition," Morel was able to attribute the most diverse illnesses in one generation to the occurrence of quite different illnesses in the preceding generation: "All hereditary illnesses are sisters."

The degenerative illness par excellence was insanity, although Morel admitted the existence of a small number of mental illnesses which were not degenerative. He claimed to have determined changes in the head, eye, ear, genitalia and intestines which were infallible stigmata of degeneration. On the basis of his theory Morel created a new and, according to him and his friends, aetiological classification of the insane into: impulsive eccentrics, "manie raisonnante," instinctive maniacs, idiots and cretins. Morel not only influenced Griesinger but also found devoted followers in Germany in R. von Krafft-Ebing (1840-1902), best known for his studies of sexual perversions, and H. Schüle, through whom he influenced German psychiatry for several decades. These wildly exuberant theories did not prevent Morel from being an outstanding clinician and diagnostician.

His ideas were taken up in France and after 1870 were developed in particular by Valentin Magnan (1835-1916). Magnan discarded the religious side of Morel's concept and interpreted degeneration as regression in the Darwinian sense. Because of Magnan's immense prestige, judged by some to equal that of Kraepelin, the idea of degeneration dominated French psychiatry for several decades. Magnan had first studied degeneration in alcoholics; he also performed useful animal experiments in alcoholism. The predominant interest of psychiatrists of this period in alcoholism (see also e.g.

Forel, Bleuler, Kraepelin) and the degeneration hypothesis are closely related. Magnan came to the conclusion that all obsessions and compulsive neuroses and all delusional states were syndromes of degeneration. He also believed in numerous anatomical, physiological and intellectual stigmata. At the same time, he put forward an interesting three-level theory of nervous physiology and pathology (first level, intellect, i.e. cerebral cortex; second level, sensitivity, i.e. basal ganglia; third level, spinal) which is extraordinarily reminiscent of the ideas of his contemporary, John Hughlings Jackson (1834-1911), the English neurologist. In degeneration, according to Magnan, the equilibrium between the three levels was disturbed. It will be evident that the degeneration theory devalued the mentally ill.

Magnan is by no means the only prominent psychiatrist to campaign against alcoholism. Forel, Kraepelin and Bleuler, among others, did likewise and to this we shall return later. Here it should be mentioned that the secret temperance society of good templars was founded in Boston in 1826 and in England in 1832, and that the Blue Cross was established in Germany in 1887. Hospitals for alcoholics have existed in Germany since 1851 (in Dusseldorf), in the United States since 1854 (Maine), and in Switzerland since 1889 (Ellikon).

The heyday of the degeneration hypothesis coincided with the vogue for discussing the relationship between genius, insanity and crime. Felix Voisin (*"Des Causes Morales et Physiques des Maladies Mentales,"* Paris, 1826, p. 4), a pupil of Gall, had already drawn attention to this relationship. A connection between mental illness and genius had been repeatedly postulated since the days of Aristotle. Moreau de Tours, one of the fathers of the degeneration theory, took up the question again in *"La Psychologie Morbide dans ses Rapports avec la Philosophie de l'Histoire"* (1859). Genius for him was simply a neurosis. Magnan followed his lead. The degeneration theory seemed to provide a simple explanation for this relationship. Both the genius and the madman were degenerates, with the difference that the genius was a "dégénéré supérieur." At this stage Lombroso (1864) and Max Nordau appeared on the scene and dealt with the same question in their popular books which met with such tremendous acclaim. (For a more recent and unusually thorough study of the problem itself see W. Lange-Eichbaum: *"Genie, Irrsinn und Ruhm,"* Munich, 1956).

People had believed in a criminal physiognomy since Aristotle. Vauvenargues and Cabanis had already identified crime with madness. Gall had regarded a large proportion of criminals as congenital, had found in them certain physical stigmata, and had suggested reforms of the penal code which later became famous in association with the name of Lombroso. To considerations of this problem too the degeneration theory gave a new impetus. Morel and Moreau believed that the same hereditary predisposition was present in criminals and in the insane, and in both it was, of course, a matter of degeneration. Only then did the Italian psychiatrist, Cesare Lombroso (1836-1909), take up the question in his *"Uomo delinquente,"* thus becoming the creator of criminal anthropology. His own contribution consisted solely in his interpreting degeneration on evolutionary lines as atavism, so that he regarded criminals as a kind of surviving primitive race. Rarely has a psychiatrist achieved such fame on the strength of other men's ideas. Lombroso was strongly supported by the psychiatrist Leonard Bianchi (1848-1927) who became a parliamentary delegate in 1892 and was made minister of education in 1905 and of health in 1917. Italy acquired asylums and university departments of psychiatry early but equipped them poorly. To this day her psychiatric orientation remains a somatic one.

Towards the end of the century the degeneration theory began to lose credit in psychiatric circles. Ziehen and Kraepelin, although still much influenced by it, expressed numerous reservations. Konrad Rieger (1855-1939) opened the direct offensive against it (1892). The work of Stieda and Schwalbe showed that many "stigmata" were simply normal variations of no pathological significance. The comparative studies of Diem and Jenny Koller discredited certain false ideas about heredity which had turned even progressive paralysis into a degenerative hereditary disease. Experience failed to confirm the concept of progressive degeneration either in families or in nations.

The degeneration theory of "polymorphous" heredity was finally exploded by the new and more accurate knowledge of the actual mechanisms of heredity, which spread rapidly as a result of Mendel's experimental work and its revival at the beginning of the twentieth century. The beautiful dream of a new synthesis was over. The works of Genil-Perrin (1913) and Oswald Bumke (1912) can be regarded as the epitaph of the classical degeneration theory. The pseudo-problem of degeneration gave way to the real, difficult and still much debated problem of the genetics of mental illnesses from which it originally derived, and twin studies in particular have led to valuable new knowledge. Regrettable and unscientific by-products of genetic studies such as the Nazi law "for the prevention of hereditarily tainted progeny" have disappeared too. The curious concept of degeneration however, which had raised so many hopes in psychiatry and met with such unexpected acclaim, still remains alive in the mind of the general public and also re-emerges from time to time under various guises in scientific works.

Darwin's and Herbert Spencer's concept of evolution had not only made the degeneration theory popular but also stimulated the English neurologist, John Hughlings Jackson, to explain epilepsy on the basis of an evolutionary three-level theory of the central nervous system (lowest level, spinal cord and medulla; second level, basal ganglia; third level, frontal cortex). In epilepsy and mental illness there was cessation of function of an upper level of the central nervous system and continued function of a lower level. Jackson's theory, which was not entirely new, exerted a tremendous influence on neurophysiology, neurology and psychiatry from the turn of the century. It was influential even in such specialties as psychoanalysis and "psychosurgery," particularly since it seemed to be borne out by the large-scale observations made on post-encephalitic states after 1918. Jackson's theories constituted probably the most successful application to medicine of the concept of evolution.

CHAPTER VIII

GERMAN PSYCHIATRY IN THE FIRST HALF OF THE NINETEENTH CENTURY

WE turn now to German psychiatry which was to take the international lead in the second half of the nineteenth century. In the early nineteenth century German psychiatry, like the whole of German medicine, was dominated by the spirit of romanticism. August Hirsch went so far as to consider it to be the best part of German romantic medicine. The ravages of two national defeats: the first external, the second internal, had led in Germany, as often happens under these circumstances, to an intensive flight into metaphysics and mysticism. It is no coincidence that so many psychiatrists of this period were also poets, nor that Paracelsus's reputation in Germany now underwent a radical change. Kurt Sprengel had still discussed him quite soberly. One can hardly say that this new trend in German medicine and psychiatry was a profitable one, particularly if one compares its results with those achieved in France by other means at the same time. It cannot be denied that some fruitful and even some brilliant ideas lie hidden in the morass of romantic concepts but it requires almost superhuman efforts, of which only few are capable, to disentangle these ideas from the speculative and moralistic verbiage of the period. The temptation has always existed to conceal ignorance beneath a cloak of empty and esoteric words, instead of frankly and humbly admitting it. But rarely has this temptation been so much indulged as in the early nineteenth century.

The romantic movement in psychiatry found its purest expression in the psychic school, so called because its members regarded mental illnesses as diseases primarily of a disembodied soul. They engaged in bitter strife with the somaticists who for their part treated mental illnesses as if they were purely physical disorders with more or less important psychological symptoms. It is as well that the romantic psychiatrists were known as "psychicists" because it would certainly be wrong to regard them as psychologists. What they called psychological was largely moralistic, while strangely enough, what the French in this period designated as "moral" was largely psychological.

Many leaders of the romantic movement in medicine, e.g. Windischmann, Leupoldt or Ringseis, saw every illness as the result of sin.[1] The most prominent representative of this movement in psychiatry was J. Heinroth (1773-1843) who wrote poetry under the assumed name of Treumund Wellentreter. His text book appeared in 1818. He regarded mental illness purely as a disease of the soul and essentially as a "lack of freedom." God had punished the sinner by depriving him of his freedom of will. With such a piece of sophistry this curious psychiatrist came to the conclusion that the mentally ill are in fact responsible for their actions. Logically enough he rejected hereditary factors as playing a part in mental diseases because each individual is always provided with a new soul. Despite his occasionally brilliant but soon forgotten aperçus, it would be incorrect to regard him as one of the fathers of psychosomatic medicine, although he did coin the word. His importance lies rather in the fact that he took over developmental ideas along with other romantic speculations and applied them to psychiatry. Some of his formulations are impressive, e.g. "Wie der Mensch liebt, so lebt er." Heinroth also concerned himself with classification ("the science of form") and found thirty-six different kinds of mental illness. Apart from the religious there were the ethical psychicists such as K. Ideler (1795-1860). Ethical insight and behavior were for him the ultimate criteria of mental health. Mental disease was brought about by unbridled passions and was the expression of "an extreme degree of individuality." A further group of psychicists consisted of the psychologists, such as F. E. Beneke (1798-1854), who used such speculative concepts as changes in psychic space. Others, like Haindorf and Kieser, indulged in more general speculations about polarity, etc. The regressive element in romantic psychiatry is most clearly illustrated by the fact that Justinus Kerner (1786-1862) and K. K. Eschenmeyer (1768-1852) went so far as to revive the concept of possession and once more to recommend exorcism. Kraepelin explained the romantic movement

---

[1] See also Siebenhaar, W. von., *Krankheit als Folge der Sünde*, Hanover, 1950.

in psychiatry on the basis of a lack of experience. This may have been true for some of its representatives. It was certainly not true for a great many of them. They were all familiar with the great French collections of empirical material. The fact remains that despite their occasional expressions of approval of knowledge gained from clinical experience, this was for them of less importance than their idealistic constructs.

The smoaticists, e.g., Friederich Nasse (1778-1851), had a much more down-to-earth approach. Nasse continued indefatigably in his task of founding psychiatric periodicals which his teacher, Reil, had begun in 1805. Nasse was particularly interested in the psychological functions of the heart. J. B. Friedreich (1796-1862) based his work on the old theory, now once more in vogue, that psychopathy springs from temperament. Maximilian Jacobi (1775-1858) was interested in all somatic manifestations of mental disease, especially in pulse rate and chemical changes. He had several very gifted pupils, among them F. Bird. His *"Observations" appeared* in 1830. With reference to Nasse and Jacobi, Joachim Bodamer correctly pointed out that all the somaticists and later even Griesinger showed some romantic and idealistic traits.[2] They arrived at their somaticism only because they were convinced that the immortal soul could not become diseased. Fundamentally the somaticists and psychiatrists were equally speculative[3] and equally unproductive. It would be wrong however to look for the origins of the psychic school only in the spirit of the age; the sterility of somaticism certainly contributed to its development.

Groos and Blumroeder attempted a speculative mediation between the psychicists and the somaticists. Even in Feuchtersleben's (1806-1849) late attempt at a compromise (1845) one can still clearly distinguish the moralistic and metaphysical elements of romanticism. Apart from this Feuchtersleben worked largely on the basis of the concept of coenaesthesia (inner sensory impressions) which had been current in France since the time of Cabanis. The concept of coenaesthesia was used to link up purely external influences with spontaneous psychic activity.

German administrative psychiatry flourished during this period.

2 Bodamer, J., Zur Phänomenologie des geschichtlichen Geistes in der Psychiatrie; Nervenarzt, 19: 229-310, 1948.
3 Birnbaum, K., Geschichte der psychiatrischen Wissenschaft. in Bumke, O., Handbook of Mental Diseases; Vol. 1, p. 30, Berlin, 1928.

Modern institutions were opened everywhere, e.g. in 1811 Sonnenstein, in 1825 Siegburg (under the direction of Jakobi), in 1830 Sachsenberg (under the direction of K. Flemming, 1799-1880), in 1834 Winnenthal (Superintendent: A. Zeller, 1804-1872, Griesinger's teacher), in 1836 Halle (under the direction of H. Damerow, 1798-1866, a pupil of Esquirol), in 1842 Illenau (Superintendent: Christian Roller, 1802-1878). Guggenmoos, the teacher, opened the first school for cretins in Salzburg in 1816 and J. Guggenbühl (1816-1863), in the face of much opposition, built the first institution for cretins on the Abendberg near Interlaaken in 1840. During this period 30 institutions were opened in Germany, 18 in France and as many as 38 in Great Britain.

Thus the directors of institutions, whose speculations were constantly exposed to the test of reality through their daily contact with the patients among whom they lived, became the leaders of German psychiatry[4] between 1830 and 1860. Three of the best known (Damerow, Roller and Flemming) founded the *"Allgemeine Zeitschrift für Psychiatrie"* in 1844, taking as their model the French *"Annales"* with whose editors they were in close contact. This was the first German psychiatric journal which was to survive. Except for the somaticist, Flemming, their philosophy was an anthropological one based on the unity of mind, body and soul. They rejected a purely mechanistic viewpoint and thus constituted a transitional generation between the romantics and the mechanists. Griesinger was responsible for the triumph of mechanism. German "institutional psychiatry" was taken over by German "university psychiatry" and as such attained international renown.[5] In France too these changes took place but here they occurred later and less conspicuously.

The use of all too active treatment methods persisted into the first half of the nineteenth century and included the revolving chair to which the most varied names were given. "Nausea" and "pain" therapies were also used, as was the douche. E. Horn (1774-1848), who is regrettably famous for his special sack and his method of forced standing, used to drench his patients at the Charité at Berlin

4 Bodamer, J., *Zür Entstehung der Psychiatrie als Wissenschaft im 19. Jahrhundert. Fortschr. d. Neurologie-Psychiatrie,* 21: 511-534, 1953.

5 K. Jaspers is responsible for the concepts of "Institutional Psychiatry" and "University Psychiatry": see his brilliant historical chapter in his *"Allgemeine Psychopathologie,"* Berlin-Heidelberg, 1948, pp. 703-716.

with not less than two hundred pails of water at one sitting.

Wilhelm Griesinger was born in Stuttgart in 1817. During his high school years and his student years at Tübingen he became a close friend of the surgeon, Roser, and the internist, Wunderlich. Together with them he was to found the *"Archiv für physiologische Heilkunde"* in 1842, which became one of the most important instruments in the reform of German medicine in the mid-nineteenth century. After studying at Tübingen and Zürich, Griesinger worked for two years with Zeller at Winnenthal. On the basis of his experience there, he published the first edition of his *"Pathologie und Therapie der Psychischen Krankheiten"* in 1845. The last edition to appear in his lifetime was that of 1867. In 1843 he was made Professor of Internal Medicine at Tübingen, and in 1849 at Kiel. From 1850 to 1852 he was physician to the Egyptian Khediv and Director of Medical Services at Cairo. His famous book on infectious diseases (1857) is based on his experiences and discoveries there. He returned once more to become professor of Internal Medicine at Tübingen and Zürich, and in 1865 he moved to Berlin to occupy the chair of Psychiatry and Neurology. He died only four years later, in 1869.

Griesinger begins his *"Pathologie und Therapie der Psychischen Krankheiten"* (Translation by C. C. Robertson, *New Sydenham Society Publications,* No. 33, London, 1862) with a plea for the localization of mental diseases and their symptoms. There is no doubt in his mind that the brain is the seat of mental diseases, although it has not yet been possible to discover specific brain damage corresponding to individual mental disorders: "Psychische Krankheiten sind Erkrankungen des Gehirns" ("Psychological diseases are diseases of the brain"), "Das Irresein ist nur ein Symptomkomplex verschiedener anomaler Gehirnzustände" ("Insanity is merely a symptom-complex of various anomalous states of the brain"). Unfortunately, he said, the knowledge of cerebral disorders is still in the stage of the knowledge of respiratory diseases before the time of Laennec. Of course not all cerebral diseases manifest as mental diseases. The diffuse cerebral disorders are most likely to do so. Psychiatry must become an independent discipline and its attitude must be a medical one and not poetic or moralistic. Although he recognized psychological causes for mental diseases, he warned against over-rating them at the expense of physical causes.

In his "physiopathological preamble" he states that all sensory impressions are transmitted to the brain where they are converted into concepts, general pictures and abstractions. Concepts in Herbart's sense can also arise from within the brain. One may be quite unconscious of such concepts, indeed the larger and more important part of mental events is unconscious. Complementary phenomena can occur after protracted emotional experiences or concept formation just as they can follow prolonged sensory stimulation. Memory is the reproduction of past concepts as a result of an association of ideas. The function of reason depends largely on memory.

Cerebral irritation leads to abnormal concepts and actions. Irritation of the contents of the abdominal cavity can result in cerebral irritation. (This is almost pure Broussaisism: Not in vain had Griesinger spent two prolonged periods in Paris.) These irritations lead at first to emotional rather than intellectual disturbances.

It is valid to compare psychological pain, a basic phenomenon of mental illnesses, with physical pain. Psychological pain depends upon cerebral irritability. An inflamed nerve is sensitive even to very small stimuli. Psychological pain is a "sensory" phenomenon. The patient invents false concepts (deliria) in order to explain this pain. The "sensory" experiences then result in appropriate motor, i.e. willed, behavior. The instincts are found at an intermediate level between simple reflex actions and behavior which results from these complicated sensory-motor relationships. In insanity, instincts are uncontrolled.

Just as Romberg had based his classical text-book of mental diseases (1840) on Bell and Magendie's discoveries (1822) about sensory and motor tracts, so Griesinger based his system of psychiatry, which is essentially a form of reflex theory, upon the same discoveries and upon Marshall Hall's subsequent experimental investigations and findings concerning reflexes (1837).

In the exposition of his views Griesinger passes imperceptibly from anatomy to physiology and thence to psychology—his "ego" psychology. He describes different developmental stages of the "ego" which he regards as being made up of a number of different conceptual elements. The ego, according to him, develops into a specific structure. It is in the healthy state capable of reflection. A man with a happy nature is one who finds it easy to harmonise the many different traits of his ego (e.g. a religious man or an empiricist) and to play any of the roles potentially present in his ego. If the ego becomes sick as a result of new emotional experiences, drives and concepts, it reacts at first by resisting these new and pathological ideas with a strong and usually sad emotion. Gradually however the ego gives up the struggle, becomes changed and finally destroyed. Once the ego has undergone a structural change, recovery is impossible. Only a strong ego is free, that is, responsible in the legal sense. Griesinger here talks in terms of psychic tonus, of faster and slower contractions. He discusses the two-way relationship between affective and somatic changes. The strongest affects, such as fear and fright, are both somatic and psychological in nature. Emotions, which can precipitate physical illnesses or can make them worse, can also be caused by them, and herein lies the key to the complex development of what we call mental diseases.

In the insane certain moods, sensations and decisions arise from within and are not based on external stimuli as in the normal person. At times however such unmotivated states of grief, gaiety and excitement are known to occur also in health. This gives us some understanding of the patient although several of his experiences are not accessible to the normal person.

After this survey Griesinger begins his detailed analysis of disturbances of mood, thinking, will, sensations and motor behavior. Mental disturbances, he says, often begin with states of fear. A happy madness often follows states of depression; the patient becomes irritable, his character alters, he becomes blunted, his relationships with others are changed.

Disturbances of thinking include retardation and quickened, confused thought; memory often remains unimpaired. If hallucinations occur, these follow the trend of the patient's original concepts; whether he believes he is being persecuted by witches, freemasons or magnetists, depends on his educational level and his attitudes to life. Disturbances of mood are followed by deep-rooted, false beliefs and the patient's condition now becomes stationary. All fixed ideas have reference to the self and are an expression either of restriction (even then translated into the English word "frustration") or gratification of the patient's mood and wishes. Many historical ideas which appear to us to be delusions (e.g. a belief in witchcraft) were not the result of mental diseases. Their psychological basis was completely different. Griesinger criticises Esquirol's idea of monomania. He holds that the psychological unity is always destroyed, even if formal examination reveals only a disturbance of part functions.

Disturbances of the will vary from its total absence (stupor) to over-activity and ecstasy. Griesinger again compares this situation with the reflex. He mentions Leubuscher's abulia. Instinctual drives towards motor activity are powerful. The question of legal responsibility (absence of free will) is concerned not so much with automatic, compulsive behavior, as with states of great excitement or upsetting perceptual disturbances. Griesinger here once more draws a parallel between normal and pathological mental events and discusses kleptomania as described by Jacobi.

As far as primary disturbances of perception are concerned, the patint may feel himself to be ill or well. Often he has the feeling that the body he inhabits is not his own. Areas of anaesthesia are frequently found, and not only in hysterics. Hallucinations and illusions are of course typical disturbances in the perceptual sphere. Hallucinations are certainly in part organically determined but can also occur in normal people. He refers here to Pascal, Spinoza, Goethe, Jean Paul, Walter Scott, Johannes Mueller, Andral and many others.

Normal people have many experiences analogous to states of insanity, for example in dreams, during febrile delirius and in toxic states. While dreaming and in the delirium of mental illness one reacts to bodily sensations without being aware of doing so. In both states critical faculties are lost and in both we notice the gratification of wishes which, unfulfilled in reality, had been repressed. Sleep induced by magnetism and somnambulism are also allied to states of insanity. Recovery may take the form of "awakening" but may also take the form of a prolonged struggle.

In the general diagnosis of mental diseases the following facts should be remembered: the ego, the personality, undergoes a change; it becomes estranged from itself, alienated. In order to be able to assess this, it is of course necessary to know something about the patient's previous personality. It is difficult to diagnose the disease process if its course is a slow one. It is also often difficult to differentiate it from borderline and transitional mental states and from ordinary eccentricity or immorality. Not everything that looks like mental illness is in fact mental illness. The diagnosis is made easier by a history of previous attacks or by the absence of external causes. Insanity is primarily an abnormal reaction on the basis of internal causes.

The diagnosis should be based on the general impression of the patient rather than on the presence of a single symptoms. Beliefs in witchcraft or eternal damnation may be normal for one individual and pathological for another. Raving madness (mania) is character-ized by excitement, melancholia by depression, and dementia by weakness of though. Hallucinations, headaches, insomnia and con-vulsions may appear. All symptoms of cerebral disease are especially important in diagnosis. One must of course be prepared for simula-tion, since patients who are mentally ill in one way often resort to simulation of another illness. One will often be confronted with borderline states and one must differentiate between mental ill-nesses and typhus, intoxications and acute meningitis. Once he has made a diagnosis of mental disease, the clinician should always ask himself which part of the brain has been affected.

In order to determine the causes of insanity we must examine the past history of the individual, with respect both to his physical and his mental development. Mental illnesses are usually brought about by multiple causes. The seed of the illness is often laid down in that early period of life in which character formation begins. Several causes (such as shock, alcohol, worry) act on the brain and illness is then precipitated by a particular situation. Griesinger also still maintains the old distinction between idiopathic (which he calls protopathic) and symptomatic (deuteropathic) insanity.

Different nations appear to have different predispositions to mental disease. Griesinger believes that the increase of mental ill-ness is not merely an apparent one. The harmful effects of civil-ization are however partly compensated for by the advances it pro-motes. Political influences are not a cause of mental disease although they can be recognized in the content of the patient's deliria. He next discusses the effects of season, sex, age and social status. He points to the danger of imprisonment and particularly of solitary confinement.

Among the special predisposing causes he gives first place to heredity. Sometimes conditions are attributed to heredity which are, in fact, due to an upbringing which has been either too strict or too lenient (Ideler). Predisposing causes are also found in the psychic or somatic constitution, particularly in the "nervous con-stitution" which is characterized by irritability and weakness or by a hypersensitivity to psychological pain. As a result of many per-sonal observations, he agrees with Fodéré and Lallemand that sexual difficulties in childhood may result in this type of constitu-tion. He also mentions anaemia, shock and grief. How these causes act on the brain is unknown. He no longer believes in the great significance of cerebral hyperaemia which, until then, had generally been regarded as very important.

The most common causes are psychological in nature, and they are usually precipitating causes, or of fairly recent origin. Passions and affective states are much more often responsible than the notorious "intellectual strain." The first question Pinel always asked his patients was: have you recently had to suffer anger, grief or annoyance? If the conceptual complexes of the ego are seriously disturbed, conflict arises in consciousness and thus a split occurs in the ego. Psychological causes can act directly or indirectly via one of the organs of the body. Insomnia is a dangerous symptom.

Alcoholism must be regarded as a mixed cause since its effects may be physical and yet it may itself be caused by or give rise to grief. Dipsomania, that is periodic drunkenness, is a symptom and not a couse of mental illness. Sexual excesses also belong to the group of mixed causes. Masturbation may be harmless but can also be a cause or a symptom of mental illness.

Among the physical causes Griesinger gives first place to other diseases of the nervous system such as epilepsy, apoplexy, head injuries, nerve injuries, spinal neurosis or hysteria. Lack of sexual gratification, according to him, has been over-rated as a cause of hysteria since hysteria is quite common among married women. The physical causes comprise acute febrile illnesses and chronic constitutional diseases such as anaemia, tuberculosis, pellagra, and perhaps also diseases of the heart, gastro-intestinal and genital tracts. In the case of the latter, as also in menstrual disorders, it is often difficult to decide whether one is dealing with a cause or a symptom (of mental disease). In any case the hospital doctor should carry out gynaecological examinations on his women patients. He himself had often cured hysteria in private practice by treating the uterus. Pregnancy and the puerperium can precipitate psychoses but these also depend on constitutional factors and their prognosis is relatively good. Infanticide is often an expression of unconscious aggression.

It would of course be best to classify mental disorders on an anatomical basis. Since this is not possible, classification must be "physiological." (Here Griesinger uses a word fashionable in his circle; in fact the criteria he goes on to describe are psychological.) The beginning of the illness is marked by emotional disturbances without, or with only slight, organic changes. During the subsequent course of the illness the emotional disturbances fade and instead disturbances of thinking and of volition occur and numerous organic changes are found. Mental diseases are curable only in the first stage.

In this assumption of a single psychosis with its two stages of development, Griesinger is following his teacher, Zeller; at the same time however he does provide us with detailed descriptions of hypochondriasis, melancholia, mania, monomania and feeble-mindedness. Melancholia is a form of psychic pain. Almost all psychoses, in his view, begin with states of depression. Classical melancholia is characterized particularly by ideas of persecution and is related to hypochondriasis. In hypochondriasis, in which the patient's errors of judgment concern primarily his own state of health, we find a weak will and a feeling of estrangement. It appears to be due to abdominal or genital disturbances and to dyscrasia or psychological difficulties. In true melancholia, depression is followed by feelings of distaste and even of hatred for the outside world; by feelings of estrangement and by a withdrawal into the self. The patients may be silent for years. Guilt feelings play a major role and are followed by hallucinations with ideas of persecution and by catalepsy or states of agitation. Melancholia may change into mania (Falret) or into dementia and negativism. Suicide is a danger even in children. Incidental attacks of fever may be beneficial.

Mania may take the form of raving madness, recognizable by restlessness, impulsive behavior and incoherence of ideas. In its alternative form of insanity, sensu strictiori, or "monomanie" as the French called it, one sees extravagant volitional states with hallucinations in the presence of an outward appearance of calm. The ego is here severely damaged and ideas of grandeur are common.

Griesinger subdivides the psychological states of feeble-mindedness into partial insanity, confusion (démence), apathetic dementia, idiocy and cretinism. Anatomical changes are frequently found in these cases. Cretinism, as Chatin has shown, is due to a lack of iodine in the soil. The chief complication of insanity is general paresis, as described by Bayle, Calmeil and Delaye. This is more common in men than in women. The second major complication is epilepsy.

The pathological changes found in cases of mental illness are described in detail. Most abnormalities are found in the head. Pulmonary tuberculosis is very common. The prognosis depend; upon the form and stage of the illness and relapses often occur. Jaspers has listed Griesinger among the great descriptive writers, i.e. clinicians. His book however leads one to look for his greatness in another sphere, that of a man of ideas.

Treatment should be humane and not barbaric as in the past but it could not always be mild. Physical and psychological methods must be combined and one must treat the patient and not the disease. Griesinger is a therapeutic optimist and lays much emphasis on prevention. He also believes in the importance of changing the patient's environment, particularly by separating him from his family and by work therapy. The douche should be used only as a punishment. On the other hand baths, opium, digitalis, prussic acid and datura are recommended. He is opposed to the use of phlebotomy, blistering, purgatives and emetics. One should seek to recover and strengthen the patient's former ego. It is pointless to discuss delusions and one should divert the patient from this topic. Griesinger is a warm supporter of the system of "no restraint." Finally he discusses the problem, acute at the time, as to whether special institutions for incurables (Pflegeanstalten) should be separate from hospitals (Heilanstalten).

Although exposed to the influences of the romantic movement in his youth, Griesinger, like the rest of his generation, was an anti-romantic and turned against both psychicists and somanticists in an attempt to reconcile their conflicting theories. He was an eclectic but in a different way from Esquirol and his other French predecessors. His emphasis on morbid anatomy, and thus on the unity of psychiatry and neurology, is indeed very strong. He is the father of neuro-psychiatry, of the merging of the two disciplines, and his fame today rests on this alone. But he has more to offer: he presents us with a systematic synthesis of the anatomical, physiological, psychological and clinical points of view. All current trends in psychiatry can be traced to parts of his work. As a psychologist he developed Herbart's suggestions into such brilliant and apparently modern concepts as the role of the unconscious, ego structure, frustration and wish-fulfilment in symptoms and dreams. Herbart had incidentally also made a deep impression on Johannes Müller and Feuchtersleben, Nasse, M. Jacobi and Meynert.[6] Just as Marx claimed to have used Hegel's philosophy but at the same time to have "put it on its feet" (since, idealistically, it had walked on its head) i.e. to have interpreted it materialistically, so Griesinger might have said of himself that he had put romantic psychology "on its feet."

The modern clinical approach is found in his view of mental disease as a process and not as a conglomeration of symptoms. This led him to adopt from his teacher Zeller the concept of a unitary psychosis (Einheitspsychose) with its stages of disturbed emotion and disturbed reason. He thus escaped meaningless exercises in classification. He still showed a full understanding of psychological causes. No psychiatrist before him had so consistently stressed the transitions from normal to pathological psychic processes as did Griesinger who pointed to analogies, parallelisms and borderline states, sometimes using himself as an example. This is in part a result of his general medical theories about pathology as a form of physiology but personality factors probably also played a part.

The central elements of his synthesis consist of analogies with the latest neurophysiological observations on reflexes and inhibition. The reason for this is all too clear in view of his membership of a school of reform which called itself a school of "physiological medicine."

His synthesis no doubt had a liberating effect, following as it did on the dogmatic disputes between somaticists and psychicists. Naturally there were omissions and contradictions but these seemed to pass unnoticed by his contemporaries. The effect of his book was almost exclusively to strengthen the concept of mental diseases as diseases of the brain. His great contribution to psychology was at the time either overlooked or misunderstood and in any case rapidly and totally forgotten. It is hard to say why his work was so much more influential than the simultaneous attempts at synthesis of Hagen, Sinogovitz and Feuchtersleben. In part it may have been due to Griesinger's literary gifts, in part to his personality. He was a great reformer whose influence on the practical treatment of the

---

[6] See also Jülicher, L., *Die Psychologie Herbarts und ihre Bedentung für die Psychiatrie*, Bonn 1961. Johann Friedrich Herbart, born 1776, studied at Jena 1794-1797; was tutor in Bern 1797-1800; qualified as a university teacher in Philosophy at Göttingen in 1802. 1809-1833 Professor of Philosophy at Königsberg in Kant's chair. Died at Göttingen 1841.

insane was considerable. His acclaim may in part have been due to the more general development of German medicine in his day, in part to the fame accorded him as a result of his university appointment. He and his pupils were after all the initiators of the change from institutional to university psychiatry. Whatever the causes of his success, the fact remains that through Griesinger German psychiatry won world-wide repute and began increasingly to dominate the international scene.

CHAPTER IX

BRAIN PSYCHIATRY AND THE CLINICAL SCHOOL

K. WESTPHAL (1833-1890), Griesinger's successor in Berlin, was a man with clinical, anatomical and physiological interests. In the clinical field he studied the obsessional neuroses, particularly agoraphobia, and perverse sexuality which was also thoroughly investigated by Krafft-Ebing. In the field of anatomy and physiology his name together with that of Erb is primarily associated with the introduction of the patellar reflex as a neurological sign. From an organizational point of view the period which was now to begin was that of "university psychiatry," although the building of institutions continued (41 in Germany, 40 in Great Britain, 28 in the U.S.A.). Professorial chairs were established in Berlin in 1864, in Göttingen in 1866, in Zürich in 1869, in Vienna in 1877, in Heidelberg in 1871, and in Leipzig and Bonn in 1882. As far as its orientation was concerned, psychiatry was now predominantly brain psychiatry. The most prominent exponents of this movement were Theodor Meynert (1833-1893), professor at Vienna, and Karl Wernicke (1848-1905), professor at Breslau. Meynert believed that every external stimulus set up a permanent state of excitation at a particular point in the cerebral cortex and that this was connected to corresponding nuclei in the cortex by means of association fibres. He held that psychological states corresponded to such anatomical conditions. He also postulated that the cortex and subcortical centres were mutually antagonistic: diminution of cortical function results in a decrease of its inhibitory effects on sub-cortical centres and leads to hallucinations. Hyperaemia of the cortex results in states of agitation, whereas hyperaemia of sub-cortical centres accompanied by anaemia of the cortex produces a depression of mood. On this basis Meynert created a comprehensive classification of mental diseases.

Wernicke was much concerned with aphasia, one of the three

problems which, first studied in France, were now to be intensively investigated in Germany. The other two problem areas were monomania and general paresis which will soon be dealt with more fully. Broca's discovery of the speech centre in 1861, whose existence had been postulated earlier by Gall and Bouillaud, once more raised high hopes of the possibility of localizing psychological phenomena in the brain. Aphasia thus became a very popular field of study and, using it as a model, Wernicke drew up a whole schema of psychological disturbances. There is no doubt that Meynert contributed to the field of cerebral anatomy and Wernicke must be credited with clinical achievements apart from his schema. Nevertheless Nissl's designation of this movement as "brain mythology" and Kraepelin's as "speculative anatomy" were hardly unjust. Gudden, the old brain psychiatrist (murdered in 1886 by his patient, King Ludwig II of Bavaria, a common psychiatric fate in those days), certainly had a more realistic approach to clinical questions. His standard reply was "I don't know."

In 1857 Friedrich Esmarch and W. Jessen (*Allgemeine Zeitschrift für Psychiatrie,* 14: 20-36) for the first time suggested a connection between general paresis and syphilis and reported several cases. They thereby greatly advanced progress in the problem of general paresis in Germany. As a result of the neuro-anatomical orientation in psychiatry and of the advances made, particularly in Germany, in the technique of microscopy (Virchow), an enormous literature began to develop in anatomy and pathology. Up to now this has not yielded any final answers or practical results for psychiatry and in this respect has been largely unimportant and even worthless. The writings of Westphal, Gudden, Hitzig, Wernicke, Nissl, Alzheimer, Liepmann, Brodmann and O. and C. Vogt however have led to important advances in the sphere of pure science. To do justice to the brain psychiatry of the nineteenth century we must remember that a large proportion, sometimes perhaps up to 30%, of the mental hospital population consisted of paralytics, that is, of patients with demonstrable disease of the brain. Other organic aspects of mental disease were investigated with equal persistence but with few unequivocal results. They included blood counts, blood pressure, blood chemistry, body weight, temperature and urinary changes. A large series of diffuse classifications (Schüle, von Krafft-Ebing, Meynert, Skae, Maudsley, Tuke, Blandford) followed as a reaction to the unitary psychosis of Zeller and Griesinger.

These endeavors reflected the then current trend of ideas but were largely sterile because of the special position of psychiatry. Apart from these the clinical school of psychiatry gradually emerged and was to reach its zenith with Kraepelin. The main aim of the clinical researchers was to delineate disease pictures not by means of classification of symptoms but by observing illnesses throughout their total course. The attempt to get away from the symptoms as such was not new and can already be found in Pinel and his studies on the course of mania, but only now was it successful. In this connection general paresis served as a kind of model for a uniform natural history of disease. But the successful elucidation of this and other organic psychoses, which resulted in their exclusion from the functional mental disorders, had left this latter field in complete chaos. Snell (1817-1892) was the first to attempt a formulation of new disease pictures. Stimulated by the problem of monomania he tried to prove the existence of a third primary mental disease apart from melancholia and mania which were at the time regarded as primary. This disorder he called "primary insanity" (1865). Westphal, Hagen and Sander, among others, did further work on "primary insanity" which finally gained public acceptance in the form of Kraepelin's "paranoia." Lasègue in 1852 had already isolated a "délire de persécution" and Magnan in 1883 had continued to work on this subject. Karl Kahlbaum[1] became the most eminent pioneer of this movement[2] and from 1865 onwards he was concerned with the delineation of what he called symptom complexes according to the model of general paresis. Ewald Hecker his pupil used

[1] Karl Ludwig Kahlbaum, born at Diesen (Neumark) in 1828, graduated 1855 in Berlin. After 1856, physician at the mental hospital in Wehlau and Privatdozent at Königsberg. After his academic ambitions were shattered he became director of a private clinic in Goerlitz in 1867. He died 1899. See the excellent work by R. Katzenstein, Karl Ludwig Kahlbaum, Zürich, 1963.

[2] It is one's task: "To build up disease pictures clinically so that as far as possible all phenomena manifested by the individual patient can be used to arrive at a diagnosis, and the total course of the illness is taken into account. The groups of disease patterns which thus emerge from study of the most commonly concurring symptoms, or from empirical delineations . . . were not only . . . easy to describe, they also led to a diagnostic approach which enabled one, far better than earlier classifications, to reconstruct very accurately the previous course of the illness from the present state and also to predict its further development with a high degree of probability, not only in general terms quoad vitam et valetudinem, but also in detail with respect to the various phases of the symptom picture." (Kahlbaum, K. Die Katatonie, Berlin, 1874; in Jaspers, op. cit., p. 474).

one of these, the paraphrenias, for his description a few years later (1871) of hebephrenia. Cases of démence precoce had already been described by Moreau and Morel. Another such clinical picture was Kahlbaum's catatonia which he described in 1869. Kraepelin's use of these two pictures as sub-groups of his concept of dementia praecox is well known.

Emil Kraepelin (1856-1926) graduated at Würzburg in 1878. He then became assistant to Gudden in Munich. In 1882 he moved to Leipzig where he soon gave up his neuro-anatomical studies with Flechsig and took up psychophysiological researchers with Wundt. After holding mental hospital appointments in Munich, Leubus and Dresden, he became professor of psychiatry in Dorpat in 1886, in Heidelberg in 1890 and in Munich in 1904. In 1922 he retired from his chair so as to be able to devote himself entirely to the German Research Institute of Psychiatry which he had created. Kraepelin undertook several extensive journeys abroad: to Java, India, the United States of America and Mexico in order to study mental diseases and administrative psychiatry in those parts of the world. He also became famous for his practical work, e.g. his fanatical campaign against alcoholism which was supported by so many prominent psychiatrists of the time, Forel and Bleuler among them.[3] He exerted a decisive influence over the whole future development of psychiatry through his textbook, which appeared in one volume for the first time in 1883 as the *"Kompendium der Psychiatrie,"* but which finally reached several volumes and attained its "classical" form only in 1899.

Even on the first page of his great work Kraepelin stated quite clearly that it is essential to know the clinical disease pictures, and that such knowledge could only be derived from observations at the bedside. He also stressed the importance of being able to make a valid prognosis which incidentally was often, according to him, a very gloomy one. He clearly recognized that pathological anatomy and experiments in localization had failed to help in solving the problems of psychiatric aetiology. Despite this he never gave up the hope that animal experiments, particularly with toxic substances, such as he had carried out under Wundt's direction, would have

[3] Rather than look for romantic reasons for this phenomenon we prefer the explanation that at that time alcoholics were the only group of patients who could be successfully treated. See Debrunner, R., *Alkoholabstinenz und Psychiatrie am Ende des 19. Jahrhunderts,* Zürich, 1961.

more to contribute in this field. The elucidation of basic physical changes would not however remove the need for psychological studies. Like others who in the course of medical history were not hopeful about treatment methods, he too stressed the importance of prevention and prophylaxis. Kraepelin saw clearly the social and legal problems in psychiatry. Among the aetiological causes known at that time he distinguished between the external and internal causes. External causes, he thought, probably all acted by producing cortical damage. Here unfortunately all attempts at localization had so far failed. As external causes he mentions intoxication, exhaustion, febrile delirium, metabolic diseases, alcohol, but also emotional upsets, although he accuses Griesinger of having made too much of these. A manic depressive state, he says, can for example occur with or without a previous emotional upset. He divides the internal causes or predispositions into general factors, such as age, sex, occupation, etc.; and personal ones, particularly hereditary factors, which he considers to be very important, although here too the evidence is still uncertain. He dismisses stigmata. A faulty upbringing can, according to him, also result in a predisposition to mental disease.

After a general discussion of the manifestations of insanity (disturbances of the process of perception, of cognitive activity, etc.) , of its natural history and of the methods of examination and treatment, Kraepelin describes the individual disease pictures as he has delimited them. In the present state of our knowledge, he says, the basis for this classification can be neither pathologico-anatomical nor aetiological, nor symptomatic, but must be derived from the total picture presented by the case material.

Kraepelin distinguishes between exogenous and endogenous psychoses. In the exogenous group he includes febrile deliria; psychosis due to exhaustion; intoxications, especially by alcohol; thyrogenous psychosis; general paresis; psychosis on the basis of a cerebral tumor or abscess; and dementia praecox. This disease picture, which he had created, in which he combined the hebephrenia and catatonia of Kahlbaum with a paranoid form described by himself, and which he defines essentially on the basis of its end state, he regards as being due to "self-intoxication." Among the endogenous psychoses he lists degenerative psychoses; manic depressive psychoses, in delineating which he draws upon the earlier descriptions of Baillarger, Falret and Kahlbaum; paranoia, which he created in connection with Snell's primary insanity; the neuroses (especially hysteria and epilepsy); psychopathic states (compulsive neuroses and homosexuality); idiocy and imbecility. One does less justice to Kraepelin than to any other author in such a short review of his basic theoretical ideas. His strength lies not in theory but rather in his descriptions of disease pictures. These cannot be reproduced in a shortened version and must be read in the original in order to lead to a full appreciation of his achievement.

Kraepelin was a pupil of Wundt and he attempted to the end to base his work on the experimental method. He was also shrewd and unprejudiced enough to realize that under the circumstances prevailing at the time the surest research tool in psychiatry was the clinical study of the natural history of diseases. On the basis of these studies he constructed the three fundamental forms of functional psychoses as we know them to this day and with which the reader will be familiar (dementia praecox, paranoia and manic depressive psychosis). Even today we are not yet in a position to say whether he had thereby created something of lasting value. But even at the present time we have to acknowledge that his work has lived longer than that of any of his predecessors. He has often been blamed for his emphasis on prognosis. Historically it would be just as unreasonable to make the same charge against Hippocrates and his pupils who also laid great stress on prognosis. Surely it is a great step forward if, in a situation in which he can neither arrive at an objective diagnosis nor offer any rational treatment, a physician can at least give a fairly accurate prognosis. Kraepelin was an eclectic with somaticist tendencies which emerged especially in his studies on body weight, a subject investigated since the days of Esquirol, and in his emphasis on heredity. As a result he was often inconsistent. One finds litle discussion of psychology as such in his work and even less of psychotherapy. His limitations are nowhere more apparent than in his richly documented historical essay *"A Hundred Years of Psychiatry."* In this he dismisses as out-dated not only the iniquities of his predecessors but also their achievements. He had however great creative gifts and with these he assembled his many actual observations, like pieces of a mosaic, to form convincing disease pictures. This makes him, in our opinion, more than a "descriptive writer," as Jaspers called him in contradistinction to his "analytic" thinkers such as Wernicke. Kraepelin's work has proved to be surprisingly solid despite the harsh criticisms to which it was subjected both at the beginning and towards the end of his active life.

This is largely due to later expansions and improvements made by others. Foremost among these was Eugen Bleuler (1857-1939)[4] who demonstrated the fact that dementia praecox did not by any means always end in dementia and who thereupon converted it into the schizophrenias. Here he introduced such useful criteria as Richtungsprognose (general prognosis) and Streckenprognose (partial prognosis), which are similar to the general prognosis and Schubprognose (relapse prognosis) of Aschaffenburg. Bleuler also won great renown for transplanting Freud's theories of the unconscious into orthodox psychiatry. K. Bonhoeffer,[5] although highly critical of Kraepelin's schema, developed his work further in the special field of the exogenous psychoses, particularly alcoholism. (Among the earlier important workers on alcoholism besides Magnan we should mention Magnus Huss, 1849; Korsakoff, 1889; and Sutton, who described delirium tremens in 1813.) An unexpected development, confirmation and enrichment of Kraepelin's work, was made by another of his critics, Ernst Kretschmer (1888-1964). In his outstanding book, *"Constitution und Character"* (1924) he links two body types and two normal character types to the basic functional psychoses, schizophrenia and cyclophrenia (asthenic-schizothymic-schizophrenic; pyknic-cyclothymic-cyclophrenic). A contribution to diagnostic methods was made by the Swiss, H. Rorschach (1881-1922). His ink blot test (1921) stimulated the production of further "projective" tests.

The main aims of those who led the reaction against Kraepelin were to loosen his rigid system of classification and to enable wider factors not recognized by Kraepelin to be taken into consideration. The "Psychobiology" of Adolf Meyer (1866-1950), a Swiss working in Baltimore, should probably be interpreted in this way. The

---

[4] Eugen Bleuler, born 1857 in Zollikon near Zürich. Studied in Zürich and Munich. 1884-1885, assistant of Gudden; 1885 with Forel. 1886-1898, Director of Rheinau Hospital; 1898-1927, Prof. of Psychiatry at Zürich and Director of Burghölzli, in succession to Forel. Died 1939.

[5] Karl Bonhoeffer, born in Neresheim, Württemberg, 1868. Qualified in Tübingen, 1892; assistant of Wernicke in Breslau; 1903, professor at Königsberg; 1904 at Heidelberg and Breslau; 1917 at Berlin, where he retired in 1937. Two of his sons and two sons-in-law were executed after July 20th, 1944. Died 1948. See also Dunn, J. E., *Bonhoeffer und die exogenen psychischen Reaktionstypen,* Zürich, 1966.

GROUP OF PROMINENT GERMAN ALIENISTS AROUT 1860
Standing: Dick. Zeller. Gudden. Laehr. Stimmel.
Seated: Damerow. Kern. Martini. Roller. Flemming. Müller.

Freud with Disciples 1909

Beginning with first row, left to right: Franz Boas, E. B. Titchener, William James, William Stern, Leo Burgerstein, G. Stanley Hall, Sigmund Freud, Carl G. Jung, Adolf Meyer, H. S. Jennings. *Second row*: C. E. Seashore, Joseph Jastrow, J. McK. Cattell, E. F. Buchner, E. Katzenellenbogen, Ernest Jones, A. A. Brill, Wm. H. Burnham, A. F. Chamberlain. *Third row*: Albert Schinz, J. A. Magni, B. T. Baldwin, F. Lyman Wells, G. M. Forbes, E. A. Kirkpatrick, Sandor Ferenczi, E. C. Sanford, J. P. Porter, Sakyo Kano, Hikoso Kakise. *Fourth row*: G. E. Dawson, S. P. Hayes, E. B. Holt, C. S. Berry, G. M. Whipple, Frank Drew, J. W. A. Young, L. N. Wilson, K. J. Karlson, H. H. Goddard, H. I. Klopp, S. C. Fuller phenomenological school, both in its original form ("verstehende Psychiatrie"), as created by the psychiatrist-philosopher, Jaspers, and in its later form (L. Binswanger, E. Straus), which was much influenced by the philosopher Husserl, has no doubt contributed greatly to the understanding of the individual patient. Its reaction to the Kraepelinian system appears at times extreme (Jaspers: "Die Diagnose ist das Unwesentlichste"—"Diagnosis is of least importance"). Psychiatric phenomenology is of most significance for those with a philosophical bent.

Unfortunately Hans Berger's (1873-1941) great discovery of the electro-encephalogram (1929), so important in the field of epilepsy, also failed to yield practical results in the field of mental illnesses as such. Traumatic (compensation) neuroses became a special problem for German psychiatry after Bismarck's (1884) introduction of national insurance. This problem has been intensively investigated there since the days of Westphal and of H. Oppenheim, the neurologist. It became particularly important during the first World War when the study of brain injuries also set new problems for psychiatry. Child psychiatry began to develop into a special subject as a result of the work of Moreau, E. W. Güntz (1859), Schüle (1878), Emminghaus (1882), Kahlbaum (1884) and others, although psychiatric illnesses in childhood had been recognized both before and since Pinel and Esquirol.

CHAPTER X

FROM NEUROLOGY TO PSYCHOANALYSIS

THE position of the psychiatrist around 1900 was not a particularly happy one. Although he was better able to classify the psychoses and predict their outcome than his predecessors a century before, he still suffered from the same ignorance of the causes of mental illness and he still had to be content with the same miserable methods of treatment. If he worked in an institution or a clinic he saw only severe and hopeless psychoses, and although anatomy and physiology had been so helpful to his medical colleagues, they had failed to teach him anything about the nature of these illnesses except in the case of general paresis. His patients were prisoners and in a way he himself was a prisoner caught up in the difficulties of the field in which he had chosen to work. (From my own experience of the same situation thirty years ago I can testify that this is not an exaggeration.) He was to some extent liberated from this situation by help from an unexpected source.

It is one of the great paradoxes in the history of psychiatry that neurology, which had at first served to strengthen somaticist trends in psychiatry, should now produce the pioneers of psychogenic research. Neurology had grown up. The enormous advances made in neuro-anatomy and neuro-physiology (Remak, Waller, Magendie, Marshall Hall, E. H. Weber, Dubois-Reymond) had been translated into clinical achievements by Duchenne, Charcot and his school, Brown-Séquard, Erb, Oppenheim, Strümpell, Quincke, John Hughlings Jackson and Gowers. Most of these great neurologists were incidentally not "neuropsychiatrists" but "neurointernists." These methodical clinicians were also chiefly concerned with incurable diseases. But such diseases made up only a very small part of the material that confronted them day by day. Their consulting hours were crowded with people suffering from "nerves," and they were forced to do something for them.

In 1868 George Beard (1839-1882), an American, published his imaginative, impressive, lively and perceptive catalogue of the complaints which we now describe as neurotic, functional or psychosomatic. He interpreted them on an organic basis as due to weakness of the nervous system which he called "neurasthenia." Beard made "nervousness" fashionable throughout Europe, not only in the field of psychopathology but in art, poetry, economics and even history (Lamprecht). A. Steiner has described this very well in hìs book *"Nervöses Zeitalter"* (Zürich, 1964).

In the seventies the great Jean Martin Charcot (1825-1893), head of the Salpêtrière, who had achieved such enormous successes in the elucidation of tabes, multiple sclerosis and amyotrophic lateral sclerosis, etc., turned his attention to a functional neurosis, hysteria.[1] He studied hysteria as he had studied all other nervous diseases by careful examination of reflexes, sensation, etc., with a view to finding evidence of organic damage in cases of hysterical anaesthesia, paralyses and contractures. He made observations on so-called hysteroepileptic seizures, on choreiform attacks and, above all, on "hysterogenous" ovarian pressure pain which he regarded as a very specific manifestation of the disease. This gave scientific blessing to the operative removal of millions of ovaries from hysterical women by the adventurous surgeons of the period. According to Charcot hysteria was an hereditary disease of the internal capsule which produced "stigmata" and seizures, triggered off by the hysterogenous zones. Charcot's concept of hysteria was a tragi-comical misunderstanding. In the hands of his pupil, Babinski,[2] the innumerable specific neurological signs which Charcot had observed disintegrated and proved to have been largely based on suggestion.[3] His-

[1] Jean Martin Charcot, born in Paris 1825, son of a coach builder. 1848, interne; 1853, Chef de Clinique at the Salpêtrière; 1872, Professor of Pathology and Anatomy; 1882, Professor of Neurology; 1893, died of a heart attack. World famous neurologist and teacher. Also very interested in the creative arts. His enormous library, now unused, is housed in a side room at the Salpêtrière.

[2] Joseph Babinski, born in Paris 1857, son of a political refugee from Poland. 1881, interne; 1886, Chef de Clinique under Charcot; 1890, Médecin des Hopitaux at the Pitié. Reflex studies, especially the Babinski reflex, 1896; neurophysiology of the cerebellum. Died 1932.

[3] Babinski's definition of hysteria was as follows: "L'hystérie est un état physique spécial qui se manifeste principalement par des troubles qu'on peut appeler primitifs et accessoirement par des troubles secondaires. Ce qui charactérise les troubles primitifs, c'est qu'il est possible de les reproduire par suggestion chez

torically however this is of secondary importance compared with the fact that because of Charcot's studies hysteria once more became "respectable."

From 1878 onwards Charcot made further contributions in the field of the neuroses by his use of hypnosis in the study of hysteria (always on the same small number of chronic patients with severe hysteria at the Salpêtrière). Here again his methods were the same and his results erroneous. He considered hypnosis to be a pathological state which occurred only in hysterics and for which he invented a fantastic system of specific stages and phenomena. Here also the importance of his work lay not in his results, but in the fact that hypnosis until then despised and neglected in academic circles —hypnotic phenomena were largely regarded as pure fraud—became not only a legitimate field of study and treatment, but for a time even an object of fashion because of its use by the greatest living neurologist and the most influential French physician. The studies in hysteria and hypnosis which now began resulted in the recognition of new facts, in the formulation of new theories and, above all, in undoubted therapeutic successes. These, whatever may have been their basis, once more destroyed the apathy and hopelessness which had begun to spread throughout the whole field of neuro-psychiatry.

The following remarks summarize the early history of hypnosis: Franz Anton Mesmer (1734-1815), a Viennese physician, began in the seventeen seventies to obtain extraordinarily successful therapeutic results with a method which he called "animal magnetism" and which was also called "Mesmerism" after himself, Mesmer believed that the universe was filled with a magnetic fluid and that man's health depended upon its amount and distribution. Cures were achieved by a laying on of hands by the magnetist or through physical contact with objects, e.g. the famous "baquet," charged by him with magnetic power. On account of constant animosity directed against him Mesmer moved from Vienna to Paris in 1778. Here he at once attracted a large following because of his therapeutic successes but he was also exposed to violent accusations of

---

certains sujets, avec une exactitude rigoureuse, et de les faire disparaître sous l'influence exclusive de la persuasion. Ce qui charactérise les troubles secondaires, c'est qu'ils sont étroitement subordonnés à des troubles primitifs." Babinski attempted unsuccessfully to replace the outmoded term hysteria with "pithiatisme" (curable by persuasion).

charlatanism. After being rebuffed by a Royal Commission in 1784, which consisted, among others, of Lavoisier, Bailly and Benjamin Franklin, he retired from public life to the Bodensee.

It was of course easy to refute Mesmer's naive notions about magnetism. One fact however remained, although it may have been less important for the learned members of the various commissions which were concerned with Mesmerism in the subsequent decades than for the practical physician. This was that Mesmerism had extensive therapeutic successes to its credit. As a result it did not depart together with its creator; on the contrary, it spread throughout France, Germany, Great Britain and the United States of America. It should not be forgotten that Mary Baker Eddy, the founder of Christian Science, had for years been a Mesmerist. In 1784 a pupil of Mesmer, the Marquis de Puységur, published observations on a sleep-like state which often occurred in the course of mesmeric treatment. This was the so-called artificial "somnambulism" which is identical with what today we call hypnosis. This is really the beginning of the history of hypnosis. As early as 1815 several French Mesmerists (Abbé Faria, Deleuze, Alexandre Bertrand, Noizet) realized that psychological (imaginative) and not magnetic forces were at play in this somnambulism and that it could also be produced without the laying on of hands. It appears, however, that this notion became more widely accepted only through the book of James Braid (1795-1860), the Manchester surgeon, which was published in 1843 under the title of: "Neurypnology or the Rationale of Nervous Sleep." It is curious to recall that at the height of Mesmerism numerous surgeons, particularly James Esdaile (1808-1859) who worked in India, performed often quite major operations painlessly under the influence of hypnosis. Braid coined the terms hypnosis and suggestion and explained the Mesmeric phenomena on a "physiological" (that is a psychological) basis. His phrenological notions however limited the value of his work. Braid's ideas were made known in France by E. E. Azam of Bordeaux.

The modern approach to psychotherapy sprung mainly from the work of the "Nancy School." Charcot's orientation had not been a therapeutic one. In 1850 Dr. A. A. Liébeault (1823-1904) had established himself as a general practitioner in Nancy, and as a result of the successful application of Mesmerism in several cases he had come to the conclusion that the major factor in this was suggestion. Liébeault was a quiet man, a therapist rather than a theoretician, who published his results only in 1866 in a book entitled: *"Du Sommeil et des États Analogues Considérés surtout au point de vue de l'action du Moral sur le Physique."* This was completely ignored at the time. His methods were however studied in the eighties by the Professor of Medicine at Nancy, Hippolyte Marie Bernheim (1840-1919). He championed Liébeault's methods, attained good results from their practical application, and emerged victorious from a prolonged controversy between his school and that of Charcot. Bernheim, at first professor at Strasburg, had originally had a frankly somatic orientation, had been a pupil of Kuess and Virchow and a specialist for infectious diseases. In 1871 he moved to Nancy because he refused to continue to lecture at the University of Strasburg after it had become German. In Nancy he had no facilities (laboratories, etc.) for continuing his work in his usual manner and this was probably the reason why he then turned his attention to psychological methods of healing. The publications of Bernheim and his associates attained tremendous popularity. From all over the world young psychotherapists, such as Freud and Forel, pilgrimaged to the small and sleepy town of Nancy. It seemed that hypnosis and suggestion had at last provided a means not only of treating the neuroses but also of investigating them. Neurotic patients were largely out-patients and psychotherapy did not necessitate hospital admission. Thus just as in the seventeenth century, but for different reasons and with different results, psychiatry once more became largely a matter of "out-patient psychiatry."

In 1884 in the first edition of his *"Suggestion-therapy"* Bernheim described the methods of inducing hypnosis and said that it was not an hysterical neurosis as had been maintained by Charcot's school. He showed that their observations on hypnosis were based on artificially induced phenomena. According to Bernheim, almost everyone could be hypnotized. He regarded hypnosis as a state related to natural sleep. Just like deep sleep, the hypnotic state, he said, facilitated the carrying out of suggestions which, in the waking state, would be impeded by rational thinking, attention and judgment. He found no evidence for the transmission of anything physical during hypnosis as had been assumed by the Charcot school. Braid had already proved that one is not here dealing with any "fluid." Behnheim considered that in hypnosis the patient was under psychological influence. In both his and Liébeault's experience it was not sleep but suggestion which had proved to be the essential factor in treatment with hypnosis. The results achieved by means of hypnosis could almost all be obtained by means of suggestions made in the waking state or by means of auto-suggestion.

Bernheim undertook numerous experiments in hypnosis, e.g. with post-hypnotic suggestion (already practised by Bertrand in 1823). This seemed to him to prove the existence of latent memories and to produce interesting and quite unrealistic explanations (later called "rationalizations" by Freud) of their behavior on the part of the patients. He refused to assume an "unconscious" state, since experiences during hypnosis can be recalled to memory. Bernheim produced in hypnosis even physical phenomena like blisters on the skin and hallucinations which he called artificial dreams.

Bernheim's theory of hypnosis, which he himself described as being merely a formula, was as follows: Each human being is provided with numerous automatic (reflex, instinctual) behavior patterns which in fact predominate until the ninth month of life. Human beings are also, by nature, gullible and open to outside influences. Reflexes are normally controlled and inhibited by the brain which provides a reasonable interpretation of sensory impressions. When this cerebral control is diminished, automatic and suggested responses are released. Despite this, the ego is not completely excluded in a state of hypnosis but the reflexes come into action before it can take charge, since the state of consciousness is altered during sleep. This is also the basis of the "double life" (split personality).

Bernheim also examined in detail the implications arising out of this concept of suggestion for forensic medicine (seduction, false testimony, murder) and for education. Much of this work was in collaboration with the lawyer Liégois and the psychologist Beaunis (see Boner, A., *Suggestion et Jurisprudence,* Aarau, 1962). He showed that the effects of former methods of healing, such as the magnet which had been used even by Laennec and Trousseau, of the healing touch of kings, and of places of pilgrimage such as Lourdes, were all due to suggestion. But as to what exactly suggestion was and why it worked Liébeault and Bernheim knew as little as we do today.

Bernheim treated mainly cases of hysteria, hysterical paralysis, neuropathies and neuroses (writer's cramp, enuresis). But he also had successes in cases of organic disease such as apoplexy, gastro-

intestinal disorders, rheumatism, neuralgia and menstrual disturbances. Treatment, he said, must be adjusted to the patient. He
analyzed the causes of possible therapeutic failure.

These, because of the purely symptomatic nature of treatment
with hypnosis, were bound to increase with time and to lead to
disappointments and to neglect of the method from time to time.
Up to now however we have always returned to it in certain circumstances, e.g. in both world wars.

We cannot here describe in any detail the golden age of hypnosis
which ensued upon Charcot's and Bernheim's discoveries. Suffice it
to say that hypnosis was not only used therapeutically but also
examined experimentally, e.g. in the work of Charles Richet (1875),
Rudolf Heidenhain (1880), Preyer (1881), and that it was practised by such outstanding psychiatrists and neurologists as Freud,
Bleuler, Möbius, Albert Moll, K. Brodmann and Oscar Vogt. (The
latter subsequently attained fame mainly on account of their anatomical researches.) Auguste Forel (1848-1931), born in the French
part of Switzerland but with German as his mother tongue, was
director of the Burghölzli in Zürich and played a particularly important part as a mediator between French hypnosis and German
psychiatry.[4] In his search for solutions of psychiatric problems Forel
progressed from neuroanatomy via hypnosis to social reform (he
supported the temperance movement, sexual enlightenment, world
peace etc.). Like almost all experimenters in hypnosis Forel was
also interested in parapsychology which must be explained as a by-
product of the hypnosis movement.[5]

A wave of reaction against hypnosis and suggestion as psychotherapeutic methods began in the nineties and the writings of the
eminent German clinician Ottomar Rosenbach (1851-1902) pro-
claimed a method of treatment by persuasion and moral appeals.
This "rational waking psychotherapy" (psychagogik) reached its
height at about 1900 in the work of the Swiss, Paul Dubois (1848-
1918), who was joined by men such as Déjerine. These methods
also were successful. Pierre Janet rightly and somewhat maliciously
pointed out that the underlying principle of such methods, namely
to persuade the neurotic that his illness did not, in fact, exist, was
suspiciously reminiscent of Christian Science. To what extent sug-

---

4 See Walser, H., *Briefe von und an Auguste Forel,* Berne, 1967.

5 Müller, Toni, *Psychiater und Parapsychologie,* Zürich, 1967.

gestion played a part in the successes of this treatment could never, of course, be exactly determined.[6]

The studies in hypnosis of the eighties brought a third eminent French research worker to the fore. He was Pierre Janet (1859-1947). Janet became Professor of Philosophy at a very early age and combined philosophy with a great interest in psychology. In 1889 he became established as a neurologist in Paris. In 1903 he was made professor at the Collège de France.

He had begun researches into hypnosis in the eighteen eighties[7] and had made the interesting discovery that traumatic memories which the patient had forgotten could produce neurotic symptoms and could hinder his adjustment to reality. Such memories could be discovered during hypnosis and making them conscious led to cure. Janet published the first account of such cases in 1889. He is thus undoubtedly the father of what became known as the cathartic method of treatment. In his studies of hypnosis he came across the problem of splitting of consciousness, or split personality, and this he investigated intensively as did A. Binet (1857-1911) and the American, Morton Prince (1854-1929).

Janet continued to use his cathartic treatment method but only as one of numerous others. Although he too found that the traumatic memories of his patients often derived from sexual experiences and experiences in childhood, he warned against drawing universal conclusions from this. Sexual difficulties could in themselves be symptoms and not causes. One should fall back on the concept of the subconscious only if no better explanations for the pathological state of the patient emerged from his actual current life situation.

Janet regarded hypnosis as being parallel to natural somnambulism, that is as a dissociation of memory which enables other psychological tendencies to emerge. He believed that hypnosis could be induced only in hysterics or in intoxicated people. He defined suggestion as a reaction to certain perceptions: "This reaction consists of the more or less complete activation of a tendency which has been provoked without having been completed by the participation of the total personality." Suggestion artificially generates im-

6 For details see the excellent historical study, *"Psychotherapie,"* by J. H. Schultz, Stuttgart, 1952.

7 In describing Janet's point of view I draw largely on his *"Les Médications Psychologiques,"* 3 volumes, Paris, 1919.

pulses, that is the operation of tendencies which the patient can normally no longer produce at will. Hypnosis and suggestion can release useful automatic actions such as eating, sleeping, waking and recovery of memories. Janet used hypnosis and suggestion with his hysterics but he also used education. He regarded hysteria as more than a phenomenon of suggestion. For him it was an organic disease: "an organic split in the compact mass of sensory perceptions."

Janet, like Freud, was of the opinion that the incidence of hysteria was progressively declining and that it was no longer the commonest neurosis.[8] Most neuroses, according to him, were not hysterical in nature. They were based on exhaustion and fatigue and he grouped them together under the term "psychasthenie." The symptoms of psychasthenia such as obsessions, phobias, fixed ideas, hallucinations, depressions and compulsive behavior did not, according to him, constitute the essential nature of the illness. They were all produced by a lack of psychic energy or tension which leads to an inability to carry out certain actions. States of emotional excitement arose from an incapacity for adaptive behavior and states of profound exhaustion and fatigue were the result of states of excitement, or of the inadequacy and incompleteness of such adaptive behavior. The patients become "stuck in their actions"; they become compulsive. Janet adored economic metaphors. He talked of psychic capital, budget, etc., and said that the most "extravagant" or costly form of adaptive behavior consisted of adaptation to one's job and to one's family. His intimate studies of these problems (the mother-in-law, waiting, etc.) are highly entertaining and realistic. He regarded social behavior as being the most complex.

Fear of taking action was one of the many symptoms which Janet said could be interpreted as defence reactions, and it is for this reason that rest and isolation have been found to be so beneficial for the psychasthenic—and for his family. Because of his inability to love and to command the psychasthenic becomes dictatorial and longs to be loved. Impulsive behavior (such as erotomania or

---

[8] The so-called decline of hysteria is perhaps explicable simply by the change in diagnostic practices. Konrad Rieger, for instance, in his autobiographical sketch (1929) said that some cases which he had diagnosed as hysterical in the eighties and nineties of the nineteenth century, he would now call dementia praecox. On changes in diagnostic practice see also Dubois, P., *Les psychonévroses et leur traitement moral,* Paris, 1904, p. 11.

alcohol addiction) provides the psychasthenic with a certain amount of stimulation. Janet reports remarkable cases in which depression was cured by kleptomania. Treatment should therefore, he wrote, also provide stimulation and suggestion contains an element of this. What is called physical treatment is often in fact psychological treatment. Many cases are resistant to hypnosis so that one's main task is to lead and to guide the patient. His confused situation must be clarified and he must be enabled to live reasonably "within his small psychological means." Janet talks of educating, or rather re-educating, his patients. But, he says, this differs fundamentally from the education we provide for normal children and from suggestion.

Janet was an accurate and diligent observer, a logical thinker and an immensely fruitful, versatile and interesting writer who had a definite bent for systematization. Nevertheless he remained an eclectic. This deprived him of the drive and effectiveness of the dogmatist and system maker which we find in Freud.

Sigmund Freud (1856-1936) was undoubtedly the most renowned of all psychotherapists and psychogeneticists of the late nineteenth century. He was certainly the most famous physician in the first half of the twentieth century, just as Paracelsus, Boerhaave and Virchow had been in former periods. He moulded the ideas which emanated from France into the form in which they became an international movement. In our brief review of his life and work we are fortunate in being able to draw on the numerous, brilliantly written descriptions which Freud himself has published in this field.[9]

Freud was born in Maehren in 1856 but he grew up in Vienna. Anti-semitism flourished there at the time and he was forced into the position of an outsider at an early stage. In his early years he was mainly influenced by Ernst Brücke (1819-1892), the physiologist and friend of Helmholtz, K. Ludwig and Dubois-Reymond, in whose laboratory he worked from 1876 to 1882. Financial reasons forced him to turn to medical practice but he continued with his neuro-anatomical investigations under Meynert who, he thought, was "by no means well disposed" towards him. At this time he was an extreme somaticist. He himself relates how one day, much to

---

[9] Particularly in "Die Medizin der Gegenwart in Selbstdarstellungen," published by I. R. Grote, Vol. IV., pp. 1-51, Leipzig, 1925.

their consternation, he presented to his American students a patient with neurotic headache as a case of chronic localized meningitis.

In 1885 Freud, then barely thirty, was made lecturer in neuropathology and obtained a travelling scholarship to Paris. There he studied with Charcot and became his translator into German. He then studied child psychiatry with Baginski in Berlin and in 1886 he established himself in Vienna. Freud is known to have conducted experiments with cocaine at this time, and it was only by chance that his friend, Karl Koller preceded him with the discovery of local anaesthesia. His reports on his experiences at Charcot's clinic (male hysteria and the production of hysterical pareses by suggestion) were met with disbelief by the Vienna Medical Association ("Wiener Gesellschaft der Ärzte") .

Disappointed in the then fashionable electrotherapy, Freud turned more and more to hypnosis. At this time he worked in close collaboration with Joseph Breuer (1842-1925), with whom he had become friendly when they both worked in Bruecke's laboratory, and who was an eminent neurophysiologist and one of the best known clinicians in Vienna. In order to increase his knowledge of hypnosis Freud travelled to Nancy in 1889 and became the German translator of Bernheim. Since 1880 Breuer had observed that during hypnosis, hysterical patients can recall traumatic experiences and that the reproduction of psychic events, repressed at the time, was therapeutic. Freud now began to use this same method of "catharsis" and he and Breuer published their results in an article in 1893 and in their book "Studien über Hysterie" in 1895. Meanwhile Janet's relevant works had also appeared. In their book Freud and Breuer were still concerned to interpret their observations neurophysiologically. They called the transformation of the energy of repressed behavior into symbolic symptoms "conversion" and the liberation of encapsulated affects "abreaction."

Shortly after their joint publication however the rupture occurred between them. Freud had gradually reached the conclusion that in all his neurotics, in cases of hysteria, of actual neurosis, anxiety neurosis and neurasthenia, sexual difficulties were the cause of the illness. Breuer was not prepared to follow him so far. Freud also mentions a second reason for the rift. This was Breuer's adherence to neurophysiological explanations. Freud had perhaps never attached sufficient weight to these and it is doubtful if he was ever fully aware of the decisive nature of the step he had now taken.

Both Freud and Breuer had originally been neurophysiologists and Freud also never gave up the idea that all psychological illnesses must, in the end, be attributable to neurological processes and that one day it would be possible to treat them causally with injections and pills. His later theories often still contained neurophysiological "models." In practice however because neurphysiological and anatomical research had yielded no positive results for the psychiatry of the neuroses and functional psychoses, he resolved to confine his work first of all to the purely psychological level. His great later achievements were possible only because of this courageous decision. Breuer, who was older and more deeply involved in neurophysiology, could not take this step with him. Freud for his part was not, as is sometimes suggested nowadays, the prisoner of a mythical "school of Helmholtz" (see Paul Cranefield, *Gesnerus* 23: 35, 1966).

Freud at this time also abandoned hypnosis as a psychotherapeutic technique and used other methods of recalling forgotten memories; at first those he had learned from Bernheim. Only now did he become aware of the full role of repression in neurosis. Symptoms turned out to be substitute gratifications and the therapeutic task was no longer that of aiding abreaction but of promoting the uncovering of repressions and their resolution by conscious decisions. Both Freud and Janet were concerned to enable the patient to adjust to reality. Freud called his new technique "Psychoanalysis."

In his study of his patients' unconscious Freud now became convinced that all neuroses are not only derived from sexual experiences as such, but from sexual experiences in childhood. He was only temporarily disturbed by the fact that his patients described scenes of seduction in childhood which later turned out to be fantasies. Freud now reconstructed childhood sexuality in its so-called auto-erotic, oral, anal-sadistic and genital phases. His explanation of neurosis as a regression to an earlier level of fixation of "libido" (his vague concept of sexual energy), as well as his concept of the "Oedipus complex," the kernel of all neuroses, stem from this period. His broadening of the concept of sexuality to include all pleasurable bodily functions necessitated the notion of "sublimation." Thus he had created a selfcontained system, to doubt which was but a sign of repression in the critic. In his psychoanalytic technique Freud now used "free association" and began to study the phenomena of dreams and parapraxes in order to be able to interpret his neuroses. He recognized that the basic force in therapy was the phenomenon of transference and he did not deny that this contained an element of suggestion.

For ten years Freud stood quite alone. In 1906 he was joined by Bleuler and C. G. Jung (1875-1961). The latter edited a psycho-analytic year book. In 1910, together with S. Ferenczi, they founded the International Psychoanalytic Association. A "Zentralblatt" was edited by Alfred Adler (1870-1937) and Wilhelm Stekel (1868-1939) ; *Imago,* a journal for the application of psychoanalysis to the humanities, was edited by H. Sachs and O. Rank. In 1909 Freud gave his famous lectures at Clark University in Worcester, Massa-chusetts, which brought him his first official international recogni-tion. His way parted from Bleuler's as early as 1910. His two most gifted pupils, Alfred Adler and C. G. Jung, left him in 1911 and 1913 to develop their own systems. But despite this the psycho-analytic movement continued to grow. Freud himself referred to his later writings after the first World War as speculative. These comprised among others his papers on the death instinct, *"The Ego and the Id"* and *"From the Pleasure Principle to the Reality Prin-ciple."* Freud was influenced by Fechner early in his life but did not become acquainted with Schopenhauer and Nietzsche until later. In his later years he also investigated the psychoses although these are not very accessible to psychoanalysis. Nor of course are they amenable to hypnotism. Freud also attempted to apply psycho-analysis to art and religion (*"Leonardo da Vinci," "Hamlet," "To-tem and Taboo"*). In his late sixties he returned to general cultural studies which had originally interested him much more than medi-cine (*"The Future of an Illusion," "Civilization and its Discon-tents"*) . When in 1930 he received the Goethe prize, it seemed as if the furious hatred with which Germany had for years rewarded him for his achievements had at last subsided. Three years later however the all too familiar events took place which led to the death of Freud at the age of 83 as a refugee in London in 1939. In the same year the Germans began to murder their insane. The fact cannot be suppressed that on the "Führer's orders" and with the help of a number of psychiatrists, hundreds of thousands of men-tally ill and mentally subnormal patients were killed.

It is clear that psychotherapeutic and psychogenic ideas were in the air in the eighties of the last century. It was no coincidence that Janet and Hack Tuke in 1884, and Charcot, Déjerine and Freud in

1886 worked on so psychogenetic a subject as male hysteria. The reaction to the sterility of somaticism was unavoidable; the neurologists led it to victory because they had patients with whom one could work and make progress with a psychotherapeutic and psychological approach. The psychiatrists who saw only psychoses were in this respect confronted by a blank wall: Kraepelin had probably discovered more or less everything that could be learned at that time from psychotic patients in institutions and clinics. Later psychiatrists were able to apply to their psychotic patients the knowledge gained from the study of neurotics.

It is all too easy to identify and criticize the speculative aspects and other weaknesses of the psychogenetic movement, in particular of the Freudian system. But somaticists like Meynert had also speculated in their day. It is equally easy to predict that the pendulum will swing the other way once more unless new basic discoveries are made to save us from this endless to and fro. It is for example quite clear that Freud had stretched the concept of sexuality far beyond its reasonable limits; that he had over-estimated the significance of childhood experiences; that he was completely one-sided in his interpretation of symbols; and that the Oedipus complex, in the form in which he described it, was valid only for a particular social class in a particular place and at a particular time. Many of Freud's errors are probably attributable to his extreme determinism. He had taken this over from physiology where it may be permissible—psychopathology however has hardly reached the stage where it is applicable. Freud's over-determinism to some extent explains his dogmatism. The latter made some of his pupils appear ridiculous, and he himself was saved from this only by his literary talent and his extraordinary intelligence. Because his past experiences were those of a physiologist and scientist it is possible that he in fact knew little of his precursors who had developed certain concepts similar to his own, and that he more or less created them all anew. (It must be stressed however that, in contrast to his predecessors of the romantic movement, he was an empiricist and materialist.) It might have been better if he had mentioned his precursors. The patina of age would have made his ideas seem less revolutionary; they would have met with less resistance; and Freud himself might have viewed them more critically. As it was, he often regarded them as "revelations." The fact that in some countries psychoanalysis became a substitute religion, a church with all its paraphernalia such as pia exercitia (training analysis) etc., is a curious phenomenon but one that also had its precedents in other scientific movements, for example Darwinism.

Moreover, the therapeutic successes of the psychogenetic approach do not necessarily imply real etiological knowledge and causal treatment. The fact that the results of psychotherapy, of whatever school, are similar (65-70% improvement in neurotics, 35% in schizophrenics) is thought provoking. And it is to these therapeutic achievements that the psychoanalytic movement owes its subsequent success. It would never have attained general recognition as a "pure science." The example of Griesinger supports this view. It is quite possible that the therapeutic successes are essentially due to the same two basic mechanisms of confession and suggestion which are so little understood and which had been used to such good effect by the medicine man. Janet, appropriately enough, compared psychotherapy (excluding of course his own) with the mediaeval theriac, a strange concoction of the most varied drugs. If it worked one never knew which of its many ingredients had been responsible for the cure, and often one had to assume that the general effect was due only to suggestion.

It would however be unjust and historically incorrect to mention only the shortcomings of the psychoanalytical movement and not its achievements. The fact that many neurotics and some psychotics actually got better is a considerable achievement, whatever the cause of such improvements may have been. It was a great step forward, at a time when medicine was apt to be impersonal and mechanical, that doctors once more began to listen to what their patients had to say. Moreover, the psychogenetic movement liberated psychiatry from a state of hopelessness and sterility, and it cannot be denied that all psychiatrists of today, including the most sceptical and the most critical, have learned something from it. "Dynamic psychiatry" was no empty catchword. It represented an advance from the stage which Kraepelin had reached, of observing the external manifestations of total disease processes, to a stage at which such processes were to some degree understood. There is little doubt that at least a few of the mechanisms described will remain valid.

The increased vitality of psychiatry in the twentieth century was accompanied by advances in the field of preventive psychiatry. "Mental hygiene" had of course been practised by every psychiatrist from Pinel, Feuchtersleben and Griesinger to Janet and Freud. But it was the American, Clifford W. Beers (born 1876), who created the first organization to further this campaign. He had written a very moving account of his experiences as a psychiatric patient (*"A Mind that found Itself"*) and in 1909, with the help of William James and Adolf Meyer, he founded the National Committee for Mental Hygiene in New York. In this connection it must be mentioned that psychologists began to function in psychiatric clinics since the beginning of the century, social workers since the nineteen twenties and that group therapy was introduced in the thirties.

The so-called psychosomatic movement which developed in the thirties and whose aim was to investigate and treat the psychological causes of physical illnesses (peptic ulcer, asthma, etc.) came as a healthy reaction to the gross neglect of such psycho-physical relationships in the second half of the nineteenth century.[10] This movement originated not only from psychoanalysts (Ferenczi, F. Alexander, F. Dunbar) but from physicians (Krehl and his school, G. von Bergmann). It was a most valuable attempt once again to consider the patient, "body" and "soul," as a whole. But the belief that something entirely new had thereby been created was historically naive: almost every great physician, from Hippocrates to Charcot, had been a "psychosomaticist" and the practice of expressing familiar or inexplicable phenomena in a new and complicated terminology was a contribution of doubtful attraction and value. The term "iatropsychology," coined by Jerome Schneck with the old iatromechanics in mind, describes these exaggerated notions most aptly.

While Freudian psychoanalysis abandoned the search for somatic explanations at least temporarily, research in an opposite direction was being carried out by the famous Russian physiologist, Ivan Petrovitch Pavlov,[11] who in 1904 won the Nobel prize for his work

10 Although these circumstances have often been exaggerated. See for example Schneider, *Die Psychosomatik in der Pariser Klinik von Pinel bis Trousseau,* Zürich, 1961; Egli, M., *Psychosomatik bei den deutschen Kliniken des 19. Jahrhunderts,* Zürich, 1964.

11 Ivan Petrovitch Pavlov, born at Rjasan in 1849, son of a priest of the Orthodox Church. Studied natural sciences and medicine at the University of Petersburg and qualified as Doctor of Medicine in 1879. Became laboratory assistant to Botkin. 1884-1885, worked under R. Heidenhain and Karl Ludwig. 1890, Professor of Physiology at the Military Academy of Medicine. 1904, Member of the Academy. From 1921 obtained much government support (special institute etc.). Died 1936.

on the physiology of digestion. In the course of his studies Pavlov had discovered conditioned reflexes which are controlled by the cerebral cortex and develop on the basis of unconditioned "natural" reflexes regulated by subcortical centres. Pavlov differentiated positive, excitatory conditioned reflexes and negative, inhibitory ones. The concept of nervous inhibition, well known since the Weber brothers and J. Budge (1845), had been further developed by the Russian, Setchenov, in 1863. Radiation and concentration of cortical excitation featured largely in Pavlov's interpretations of his experimental results. At around 1900 he began to substitute his "physiological" objective psychology for the old-fashioned psychological psychology. That is, he endeavoured to make conditioned reflexes the basis of all mental phenomena. He even invented a "reflex of freedom." He himself recognized the relationship between his aims and those of certain North American psychologists such as E. L. Thorndike (born 1874) and J. B. Watson, the father of "Behaviorism" (born 1878). In 1918 Pavlov began using his methods to investigate psychopathology and, particularly from 1928 onwards, his work lay predominantly in the field of psychiatry.[12]

Pavlov was an outstanding experimentalist and his investigations into sleep, animal hypnosis and experimental neuroses in dogs are of great interest. Moreover the notion that all mental phenomena can be resolved into reflexes points to an extraordinary breadth of vision, however unlikely the basic assumptions may be. We must here limit ourselves to a discussion of Pavlov's contributions to psychiatry, although for the sake of his reputation we would have preferred to forego this. But because his work, including his approach to psychiatry, has been raised to the level of a national religion in a major part of the world, we feel compelled to inform our readers at least of its content.

In an attempt to reconcile the conflicting results of his experimental "neuroses" in dogs Pavlov at first resorted to the hypothesis that his dogs could be grouped according to the four "Hippocratic" temperaments: choleric, sanguine, phlegmatic and melancholic or, as he defined them in his animals: excitable, lively, placid and inhibited. His neuroses consisted of restlessness, whining, anorexia, and failure to condition. They were produced by simultaneous

---

[12] Pavlov's psychiatric papers have been collected and translated into English by W. Horsley Gantt, as "*Conditioned Reflexes and Psychiatry,*" New York, 1941.

inhibitory and excitatory stimuli or by very strong stimuli in dogs temperamentally predisposed to neurosis. These measures disturbed the normal "dynamic stereotypy" of conditioned reflexes. In strong, excitable dogs such stimuli led to a loss of almost all inhibitory reactions. Pavlov at first called this illness neurasthenia, later hypersthenia. In weak, inhibited dogs, on the other hand, such stimuli led to a loss of excitability which Pavlov at first called hysteria and later neurasthenia. This state could be improved by castration. While Pavlov assumed that there were only two neural levels in the dog: the cortical and the sub-cortical, he credited the human brain with a third level: the frontal lobes which contained the mechanism of speech. He distinguished two basic types in man: the artistic and the intellectual. In the artistic type, a coincidence of conflicting stimuli or an excess of stimuli leads to hysteria; in the intellectual type to psychasthenia; and in the intermediate type to neurasthenia.

Hysteria manifests itself most clearly in dogs of a weak, inhibitory type. A weakening of cortical functions releases sub-cortical impulses. If stimulation is continued sleep finally sets in. Pavlov equated hysteria with chronic hypnosis.

Pavlov engaged in extensive investigations of hypnosis in dogs. He took sleep to be a manifestation of inhibition. Hypnosis too was for him an inhibitory phenomenon, an intermediate state between sleep and wakefulness. The spread of sensory impulses of low intensity resulted in cortical inhibition. A weak nervous system tired easily. Fatigue also leads to inhibition and so does prolonged stimulation or stimulation which does not find an outlet in action. Strong stimulation results in total inhibition in an animal of a weak disposition. Hypnosis can lead to dissociation between motor and secretory functions, so that the flow of saliva may be retained as a conditioned reflex response when swallowing movements can no longer be evoked. In hypnosis the cortex is paralyzed while sub-cortical structures are still active.

Schizophrenia also is defined by Pavlov as a chronic hypnosis. For him it was the result of what he called ultra-paradoxical reflexes. He believed that he could observe schizophrenic symptoms such as blunting, negativism, stereotypy, catatonia in his hypnotized dogs and that these also displayed playful behavior, such as is found in cases of alcohol intoxication in which again the cortex is inhibited. Pavlov observed the same behavior in the ultra-paradoxically reacting animal. He regarded catalepsy as a paresis of the motor cortex due to what he called the cataleptic reflex. Catatonia was essentially defensive behavior. On this basis he explained the success of rest cures and of bromides in his dogs. Certain experiments with his ultra-paradoxical phenomenon evoked "paranoia" in his dogs. According to Pavlov one can initiate disease in certain parts of the brain without affecting the rest. He regarded senile dementia as a weakening of cortical inhibition due to ageing processes.

The reader will be able to form his own opinion on the somewhat doubtful value of these statements which despite all their experimental foundations were often speculative and reminiscent of the views of Meynert and Wernicke. These workers however had arrived at their formulations without troubling so many dogs. We know of no successful psychiatric application of Pavlov's "reflex psychiatry," except perhaps in the development of brainwashing techniques for prisoners. Here some of Pavlov's observations may have acted as the stimulus for further work. Bromide, rest cures and castration have not had the same therapeutic results in man as in Pavlov's "neurotic" dogs. It is an unfortunate consequence of the exaggerated cult surrounding Pavlov's ideas, that the early establishment of professorial chairs in Leningrad (1857) and in Moscow (1869) is rarely mentioned, and that the great achievements of Russian psychiatrists such as V. M. Bechterev (1857-1927) and G. G. Korsakov (1853-1900) have been forgotten.

CHAPTER XI

THE NEWER SOMATIC AND EMPIRICAL
TREATMENT METHODS

PSYCHOGENETIC research has increased our understanding of the psychoses but its contribution to the effective treatment of these mental illnesses has been minimal. Fortunately a series of physical treatment methods leading to real improvement in the psychoses were empirically discovered in the twentieth century. Admittedly we do not know why these methods are effective, nor have they appreciably contributed to our understanding of mental illnesses. Moreover their results may often have been over-estimated and exaggerated. Nevertheless the fact remains that they have led to the improvement and even recovery of a great many patients. In judging what follows, the reader should bear in mind that almost all these treatment methods are new and that many of the results have not been finally evaluated. Our assessment is of necessity more in the nature of a contemporary opinion than an historical appraisal such as we hope we have presented in previous chapters.

The first successful physical method of treatment was discovered in the field of general paresis, the first psychosis for which an organic basis had been found. This was fever therapy. Since the days of Hippocrates the medical literature has contained repeated references to the fact that intercurrent fever, especially malaria, sometimes leads to unexpected recoveries in cases of mental diseases, paresis or seizures. Similar observations had been recorded in cases of general paresis since 1822 when this disorder began to be recognized increasingly. As a result isolated attempts at treatment with artificially induced fever were undertaken in the eighteen-seventies. In a now classical article written in 1887, Julius Wagner von Jauregg (1857-1940), the young Austrian psychiatrist, discussed the possibility of treating general paresis with artificially induced febrile diseases including malaria. The problem was an urgent one because

101

although general paralysis was now recognized as being due to syphilis, it failed completely to respond to the usual anti-syphilitic methods of treatment.

A few years later Wagner-Jauregg put his theory to the practical test. In 1890 he began to treat paralytics with Koch's tuberculin and later with typhus vaccine. He obtained some good results but on the whole the method was found to be too unpredictable and uncertain to become generally accepted. In 1917 Wagner-Jauregg began to use malaria and in the course of the next few years he was so successful with this method that it gained general acceptance and he was awarded the Nobel prize in 1927. Malaria treatment also yielded important results for malaria research. Although since the nineteen forties it has largely been superseded by penicillin, which is simpler to administer and produces better results, malaria treatment for progressive paresis remains a milestone in the history of medicine, not only because it led to a drastic decrease in the numbers of paralytics in institutions and prevented their rapid and certain downhill course, but because it naturally acted as an encouragement and incentive for further trials of physical methods of treatment.

Among the pioneers of modern physical treatment for the functional psychoses we must mention O. Wolff and Jakob Kläsi for their advocacy of continuous narcosis in 1901 and 1922. This never became a popular treatment method because shock therapy was introduced only a few years later.[1] Again, the fact that severe psychological or physical shocks can result in recovery from mental diseases had been recorded from time to time since the days of antiquity. Artificial shock had therefore been used repeatedly as a method of treatment.[2] Most people who employ modern shock therapy reject a comparison of their methods with those of the past. Some of the old methods however were so drastic that this comparison seems fully justified. The best known of the old techniques was sudden ducking or submersion of the mentally ill patient. This was practised from the time of the Greeks until the days of Boerhaave. It was Pinel and Esquirol who abolished it. The latter

[1] Kalinowsky, Lothar. *Shock Treatments, Psychosurgery and other Somatic Treatments in Psychiatry*, New York, 1952. Sackler, Arthur M. Hay. *The Great Physiodynamic Therapies in Psychiatry*, New York, 1956.

[2] Buvat-Pochon, Christine. *Les Traitements de Choc d'Autrefois en Psychiatrie*, Paris, 1939.

commented on this method as follows: "Lorsque je l'entends pré-
scrire, j'aimerais autant qu'on donnat le conseil de précipiter les
aliénés d'un troisième étage, parce qu'on a vu quelques fous guérir
après avoir fait une chute sur la tête." (Esquirol, *Des Maladies
Mentales,* 1838, Vol. 1, p. 147). Just as drastic were prolonged cold
showers and the various rotating machines we have mentioned before. For years these two were reputed to produce good results until
they were finally given up, whether on humanitarian or practical
grounds it is impossible to say.

The first modern shock therapy was insulin shock. Dr. Manfred
Sakel (1900-1957) discovered that marked psychological improvement occurred after hypoglycaemic coma and fits produced by acci-
dental over-dosage of insulin which was often used in those days
for physiological reasons in cases of drug addiction. He now began
to employ insulin coma and insulin-induced convulsions systemati-
cally in psychotics and was so successful with this that his method
rapidly gained popularity. Sakel first used his method at the end of
the nineteen twenties and published his first results in 1933.

Another shock or convulsive method, that of intravenous cardiazol, was developed independently by L. von Meduna (1896-
1964). Meduna began his investigations in 1933 and first published
them in 1935. He started off from a false premise, that of the so-
called antagonism between epilepsy and schizophrenia, and his aim
was to cure schizophrenia by means of artificially induced convulsions. The first convulsant he tried was the traditional camphor. His
results improved when he changed to cardiazol and this method
rapidly became widely used after 1936.

After 1938 electro-shock began to replace cardiazol as a convulsant
technique. Electricity had been used for mental diseases since the
time of Perfect, but of course not in the violent form in which V.
Cerletti and L. Bini introduced it in Rome in 1938. Shock methods
were first used for schizophrenia and later for other psychoses including manic-depressive psychosis, in which disease shock treatment
seemed to achieve even better results than in the illness for which
it was originally introduced. Despite this many cases did not respond
to it. Shock treatment was responsible for many spontaneous dis-
locations and fractures, the incidence of which was diminished by
the introduction of curare by A. E. Bennett in 1940. Although their
beneficial effects are recognized, opinion about these somewhat
crude and brutal methods is still divided, particularly in view of

our ignorance of the underlying mechanisms and the well known fact that spontaneous remissions and relapses can occur in the functional psychoses. It is still debatable whether the effect of these treatment methods is symptomatic or causal, somatic or psychological.

"Psychosurgery" has not developed into a routine treatment as have shock therapies. As early as 1890 the Swiss psychiatrist, Burckhardt, had ablated parts of the cortex in mental patients with some success. Bechterev's pupil Pusepp had done the same in 1910. But this method had never become popular. In 1936 two Portugese workers, Egas Moniz (1874-1955) and Lima introduced their prefrontal lobotomy, i.e. section of the white matter in the plane of the coronal suture, on the basis of what appeared to be a somewhat primitive theory. The high repute of this operation was largely due to the energetic efforts of W. Freeman, an American, who adopted it at once in 1936 and modified it in several respects. Moniz was even awarded the Nobel prize in 1949. This operation undoubtedly improves some patients. In others it leads to such marked deterioration of personality that many people are still reluctant to use it.

All these methods now appear to some extent to be superseded by the latest advances in what is called "psycho-pharmacology."[3] Drugs have of course always been used in the treatment of mental disorders. Some organic psychoses respond to specific measures: endocrine disturbances[4] to hormones, pellagra to nicotinic acid, epilepsy to dilantin. Benzedrine and sodium amytal were popular for a short period. Most drugs however were merely sedatives with the usual drawbacks of tolerance, etc. They calmed patients temporarily by rendering them unconscious.

In the alkaloids Rauwolfia serpentina and chlorpromazine we have found drugs which quieten the patient without impairing his level of consciousness or his responsiveness unless they are given in very high doses. For about three hundred years it had been known that Rauwolfia serpentina was a drug used with success by primitive and other non-European people but it had found no place in the European pharmaceutical armamentarium. Rauwolfia serpentina had already been used by the old Indian physicians. Following the stimulus of India's political reawakening, modern methods were

[3] Kline, N. S., Editor, *Psycho-pharmacology*, Washington, 1956.

[4] Bleuler, Manfred, *Endokrinologische Psychiatrie*, Stuttgart, 1954.

used to re-investigate old Indian drugs, and in the early nineteen thirties Sen, Bose, Gupta and others began to study Rauwolfia and to praise its efficacy in cases of mental illness and hypertension. In the early nineteen fifties the drug was investigated in Europe and America, at first mainly in cases of arterial hypertension. Its hypotensive action was soon overshadowed by its psychological effects ("ataractic" or "angolytic," i.e. relieving anxiety states) .

At about the same time the angolytic effects of chlorpromazine, a synthetic drug belonging to the anti-histamine group, were being studied by French workers (1952, Laborit, Hamon, Delay, etc.) . In 1954 it reached the United States via England and Canada. Since then these drugs and their many analogues have been used on a vast scale. Their mode of action remains unknown. Many theories have been devised to explain their effects, for example that they act primarily on the thalamus, the hypothalamus and the diencephalon. The fact remains that they calm patients greatly without altering consciousness and that they often succeed in enabling old and electro-shock resistant patients to become accessible to psychotherapy or to make spontaneous recoveries. Like all innovations these drugs are probably being over-estimated at present. They are no panacea and they do have toxic side-effects. But the introduction of tranquillisers has meant that even "disturbed" wards of mental hospitals are now quiet, that the use of shock-therapy has been greatly reduced and that it is now technically possible for substantial numbers of psychiatric patients to be treated in general hospitals. The psychotropic drugs have thus renewed our hopes for even greater achievements in the future.

INDEX